THE ULTIMATE
MINNESOTA WILD
TRIVIA BOOK

A Collection of Amazing Trivia Quizzes
and Fun Facts for Die-Hard Wild Fans!

Ray Walker

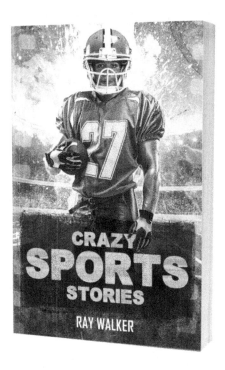

CONTENTS

Introduction 1

Chapter 1: Origins & History 3

  Quiz Time! 3

  Quiz Answers 8

  Did You Know? 9

Chapter 2: Jerseys and Numbers 12

  Quiz Time! 12

  Quiz Answers 17

  Did You Know? 18

Chapter 3: Famous Quotes 21

  Quiz Time! 21

  Quiz Answers 27

  Did You Know? 28

Chapter 4: Catchy Nicknames 31

  Quiz Time! 31

  Quiz Answers 36

  Did You Know? 37

Chapter 5: The Captain Class 40

Quiz Time!.. 40

Quiz Answers... 45

Did You Know?.. 46

Chapter 6: Statistically Speaking............................. **49**

Quiz Time!.. 49

Quiz Answers... 54

Did You Know?.. 55

Chapter 7: The Trade Market..................................... **58**

Quiz Time!.. 58

Quiz Answers... 63

Did You Know?.. 64

Chapter 8: Draft Day.. **68**

Quiz Time!.. 68

Quiz Answers... 73

Did You Know?.. 74

Chapter 9: Goaltender Tidbits................................... **77**

Quiz Time!.. 77

Quiz Answers... 82

Did You Know?.. 83

Chapter 10: Odds and Ends.. **86**

Quiz Time!.. 86

Quiz Answers... 91

Did You Know? 92

Chapter 11: Blues on the Blue Line................................**95**

Quiz Time! 95

Quiz Answers 100

Did You Know? 101

Chapter 12: Centers of Attention **104**

Quiz Time! 104

Quiz Answers 109

Did You Know? 110

Chapter 13: The Wingers Take Flight..............................**113**

Quiz Time! 113

Quiz Answers 118

Did You Know? 119

Chapter 14: The Heated Rivalries...................................**122**

Quiz Time! 122

Quiz Answers 127

Did You Know? 128

Chapter 15: The Awards Section **131**

Quiz Time! 131

Quiz Answers 136

Did You Know? 137

Conclusion...**140**

INTRODUCTION

Although the Minnesota Wild is a relatively new NHL franchise, having made its debut in 2000-01, the club still has a rabid and loyal fan base. The Wild filled the void for disappointed local supporters when the Minnesota North Stars organization moved to Dallas in 1993.

The Wild has yet to win a Stanley Cup but it certainly hasn't been through a lack of effort. They made it all the way to the Western Conference Finals in their third year of play in 2002-03 and reached the playoffs in nine of their first 18 NHL campaigns. In addition, they were crowned Northwest Division Champions in 2007-08.

The team made the postseason six years in a row between 2013 and 2018 and posted three 100-point seasons during that span.

Minnesota fans have seen some excellent players at Xcel Energy Arena over the years, such as Devan Dubnyk, Nicklas Bäckström, Marián Gáborík, Ryan Suter, Mikko Koivu, Zach Parise, and Ryan Suter. Some of them may even join former head coach Jacques Lemaire in the Hockey Hall of fame one day.

This Minnesota Wild trivia/factbook contains a wide assortment of information regarding the franchise from the day it was born until the conclusion of the 2019-20 regular NHL season.

It comes with 15 chapters, each of which offers 15 multiple-choice questions and five true-or-false statements. The correct answers are revealed on the following page. In addition, each of the chapters features 10 historical "Did You Know" facts and anecdotes about the organization's players, coaches, general managers, owners, etc.

Wild fans will be able to refresh their memories with the book and perhaps learn something they may not have been aware of. The book can also help you prepare yourself to challenge fellow fans and family members in trivia contests.

The book is designed to help remind Wild fans why they support the team so passionately and to never give up in the quest for the Stanley Cup.

CHAPTER 1:

ORIGINS & HISTORY

QUIZ TIME!

1. Who was the first president of the Minnesota Wild?

    a. Jac Sperling

    b. Doug Risebrough

    c. Martha Fuller

    d. Tod Leiweke

2. Who was the first head coach of the Wild?

    a. Todd Richards

    b. Jacques Lemaire

    c. Mike Yeo

    d. John Torchetti

3. After the Minnesota North Stars relocated, it was seven years before the state was awarded another NHL franchise.

    a. True

    b. False

4. What name was not considered when branding the new Minnesota franchise?

    a. Freeze
    b. Voyageurs
    c. Lakers
    d. Blue Ox

5. Who scored the first goal ever for the Wild?

    a. Marián Gáborík
    b. Scott Pellerin
    c. Jim Dowd
    d. Wes Walz

6. Which other expansion team made their NHL debut alongside the Wild in 2000-01?

    a. Atlanta Thrashers
    b. Columbus Blue Jackets
    c. Nashville Predators
    d. Ottawa Senators

7. Which team did the Wild make their NHL debut against on October 6, 2000?

    a. Tampa Bay Lightning
    b. Edmonton Oilers
    c. Mighty Ducks of Anaheim
    d. Phoenix Coyotes

8. Minnesota was awarded their second NHL franchise on June 25, 1997.

    a. True
    b. False

9. What was the expansion fee Minnesota paid for the Wild?

    a. $85 million
    b. $75 million
    c. $90 million
    d. $80 million

10. Which team did Minnesota try to buy in the 1990s before being awarded a franchise?

    a. Quebec Nordiques
    b. Hartford Whalers
    c. Buffalo Sabres
    d. Winnipeg Jets

11. The Wild won their first NHL game against the San Jose Sharks.

    a. True
    b. False

12. Who was the first skater selected by Minnesota in the 2000 NHL expansion draft?

    a. Sean O'Donnell
    b. Curtis Leschyshyn
    c. Scott Pellerin
    d. Jeff Nielson

13. How many goals did Minnesota score in their first season?

    a. 159
    b. 166
    c. 168
    d. 172

14. Goaltender Mike Vernon, selected in the expansion draft, became the first Minnesota Wild player.

   a. True
   b. False

15. Which arena has the Wild played in since 2000-01?

   a. Reunion Arena
   b. Metropolitan Sports Center
   c. Checkerdome
   d. Xcel Energy Center

16. When did the Wild make their first playoff appearance?

   a. 2002-03
   b. 2001-02
   c. 2005-06
   d. 2000-01

17. How many points did the Wild finish with in their first season?

   a. 68
   b. 71
   c. 59
   d. 64

18. How many playoff appearances has the club made as of 2018-19?

   a. 8
   b. 6
   c. 9
   d. 12

19. Who led the Wild in points in their inaugural season?

   a. Wes Walz
   b. Scott Pellerin
   c. Filip Kuba
   d. Marián Gáborík

20. Darby Hendrickson was the first captain of the team.

   a. True
   b. False

QUIZ ANSWERS

1. D – Tod Leiweke

2. B – Jacques Lemaire

3. A – True

4. C – Lakers

5. A – Marián Gáborík

6. B – Columbus Blue Jackets

7. C – Mighty Ducks of Anaheim

8. A – True

9. D – $80 million

10. D – Winnipeg Jets

11. B – False

12. A – Sean O'Donnell

13. C – 168

14. B – False

15. D – Xcel Energy Center

16. A – 2002-03

17. A – 68

18. C – 9

19. B – Scott Pellerin

20. B – False

DID YOU KNOW?

1. The Minnesota Wild NHL franchise is based in the city of Saint Paul, Minnesota, in the USA. The club currently competes in the Central Division of the league's Western Conference. The organization has yet to win a Stanley Cup as of 2019. The franchise was founded on June 25, 1997, but didn't make its NHL debut until the 2000-01 season.

2. The Wild isn't the first NHL franchise to play out of Minnesota; the Minnesota North Stars joined the league in 1967-68 when the NHL expanded in size from six to 12 teams. The North Stars played their home games at the Met Center in the City of Bloomington and relocated to Texas in 1993 as the Dallas Stars.

3. Since NHL hockey returned to Minnesota, the team's home rink has been the Xcel Energy Center, which opened on Sept. 29, 2000. The venue is owned by the city of Saint Paul but is operated by the Wild's parent company, which is Minnesota Sports and Entertainment.

4. The hockey team made the playoffs for the first time in 2002-03 when they reached the Western Conference Finals. However, they were swept in four games by Anaheim. As of 2019, the squad had advanced to the second round of the playoffs just twice more since 2003.

5. Minnesota came close to having its second NHL team in the mid-1990s, when a group from the state negotiated to buy

the original Winnipeg Jets franchise. The group planned to move the club to Minnesota, but arena negotiations couldn't be worked out and the Jets eventually moved to Phoenix, where they are now the Arizona Coyotes.

6. Bob Naegele Jr. applied for an NHL club when the league announced it was going to expand from 28 to 30 teams and he became the Wild's first majority owner when the franchise was awarded in 1997.

7. The new Minnesota franchise came up with six possible names for the team: The Freeze, Blue Ox, Voyageurs, Northern Lights, White Bears, and Wild. Obviously, the Wild won out in January 1998 and the club then named Jac Sperling as chief executive officer, Doug Risebrough as general manager, and Tod Leiweke as its president.

8. The Wild signed a 26-year partnership deal with the Minnesota Amateur Sports Commission (MASC), which was the first in North America between a private professional sports club and a public amateur sports organization.

9. In January 2008, it was announced that the club would be sold to Craig Leipold, the former owner of the Nashville Predators of the NHL. The NHL's Board of Governors soon approved the sale and Leipold became the majority owner of Minnesota Sports and Entertainment on April 10. Leipold had owned the Predators since 1997 and sold the franchise on December 7, 2007.

10. The Wild is associated with two minor league affiliates. They are the Iowa Wild of the American Hockey League

(AHL) and the Allen Americans of the East Coast Hockey League (ECHL). The Iowa Wild was originally located in Houston, Texas, but moved to Des Moines, Iowa in 2013.

CHAPTER 2:

JERSEYS AND NUMBERS

QUIZ TIME!

1. Which of the following jersey numbers has never been worn, as of 2020?

    a. 11
    b. 13
    c. 17
    d. 16

2. What number did Marián Gáborík wear in his rookie season?

    a. 10
    b. 12
    c. 82
    d. 77

3. The No. 1 is retired in honor of the Minnesota Wild fans.

    a. True
    b. False

4. The Wild wore an alternate jersey that was primarily what color?

    a. Red

    b. Yellow

    c. Blue

    d. Purple

5. Who was the first player to wear No. 46?

    a. Kyle Brodziak

    b. Marek Zidlicky

    c. Justin Falk

    d. Jared Spurgeon

6. In what season did the Wild introduce an alternate jersey?

    a. 2005-06

    b. 2003-04

    c. 2001-02

    d. 2002-03

7. What detail is not a part of the Wild's intricate logo crest design?

    a. The moon

    b. A river

    c. The Northern Lights

    d. A tree line

8. As of 2020, only three numbers have been retired by the franchise.

    a. True

    b. False

9. As of 2020, what is the highest number worn by a Wild player?

    a. 93
    b. 96
    c. 78
    d. 87

10. How many jerseys have been made for special event games, as of 2020?

    a. 2
    b. 0
    c. 3
    d. 1

11. In 2009-10, the Wild introduced a green alternate jersey.

    a. True
    b. False

12. Who is the only player to wear No. 67, as of 2020?

    a. James Sheppard
    b. Matt Dumba
    c. Benoit Pouliot
    d. Tom Gilbert

13. Who wore No. 19 for nine seasons?

    a. Derek Boogaard
    b. Stéphane Veilleux
    c. Jason Pominville
    d. Charlie Coyle

14. It is unknown what type of animal the team's logo is supposed to depict.

  a. True
  b. False

15. Who wore No. 22 from 2014 to 2019?

  a. Justin Fontaine
  b. Gustav Olofsson
  c. Nino Niederreiter
  d. Cal Clutterbuck

16. What number did goalie Nicklas Bäckström wear from 2007 to 2015?

  a. 31
  b. 35
  c. 30
  d. 32

17. This goaltender never wore No. 35.

  a. Darcy Kuemper
  b. Manny Fernandez
  c. Anton Khudobin
  d. Josh Harding

18. Brent Burns wore which number in his seven years with the Wild?

  a. 8
  b. 18
  c. 48
  d. 88

19. What number did Nick Schultz wear in Minnesota for 10 seasons?

    a. 35

    b. 25

    c. 55

    d. 15

20. In the 2011-12 season, Minnesota wore "shells" over their pants to match their alternate jersey.

    a. True

    b. False

QUIZ ANSWERS

1. B – 13

2. C – 82

3. A – True

4. A – Red

5. D – Jared Spurgeon

6. B – 2003-04

7. C – Northern Lights

8. B – False

9. B – 96

10. D – 1

11. A – True

12. C – Benoit Pouliot

13. B – Stéphane Veilleux

14. A – True

15. C – Nino Niederreiter

16. D – 32

17. D – Josh Harding

18. A – 8

19. C – 55

20. B – False

DID YOU KNOW?

1. The Wild's two primary jerseys are predominantly green and gold with red trim as well as white and green with red trim. Technically, the colors are listed as forest green, harvest gold, iron range red, and Minnesota wheat. The club wears green pants with both jerseys. When wearing their green jerseys, their socks are predominantly green with gold and red trim. While wearing their white sweaters, the socks are white with green trim.

2. The Wild used the same logo for the first 13 years of existence; it included the team name at the top. After that, the team name was removed from the logo. The logo itself is something of an optical illusion as it is a dusk setting that features a star in the sky inside of a forest landscape. The star represents the North Star and it also acts as the eye of a mythical wild animal in the emblem. The logo also features a river, the moon, and trees.

3. In 2003, the club came out with an alternate jersey that was primarily red. Another alternate/third jersey was introduced in 2009 which featured the words "Minnesota Wild" across the chest. In 2013, they updated the lettering on the jerseys to a more modern design.

4. In 2007-08, the NHL switched to the Reebok Edge uniform system. The Wild's white jerseys stayed the same, but the green version was slightly altered as an imprint of their

primary logo that was placed inside a white circle was surrounded by the words "Minnesota Wild." This was then placed inside a larger circle on a green background.

5. In June 2017, the club introduced a new home uniform when the NHL switched from the Reebok brand to Adidas. This was a green jersey that featured the club's main logo with a wheat-colored stripe going through the center of the sweater. The arms also featured a wheat-colored stripe along with a small red stripe at the top. However, the NHL didn't use alternate jerseys in 2017-18.

6. The most popular jersey numbers in team history so far have been 6, 19, and 26 with 12 different players wearing each of them as of 2020. Those who have worn No. 6 include Ryan Murphy and Ryan Donato. Dominic Moore and Martin Hanzal have been among those wearing No. 19, while those who have donned 26 include Thomas Vanek and Matt Moulson.

7. No. 13 is typically considered to be an unlucky number in some cultures and areas of the world. That seems to be true in Saint Paul because no Minnesota Wild player has ever worn jersey No. 13 as of 2020.

8. The franchise has retired the No. 1 jersey in honor of its team's fans. In addition, the No. 99 was retired by the NHL to honor Hall of Famer Wayne Gretzky, the all-time leading scorer in league history. No other jerseys have been retired by the club.

9. Every number between 2 and 49 has been worn by at least

one player since the Wild joined the NHL. As mentioned, the only exception is No. 13. In addition, 22 different numbers between 51 and 96 have been worn at least once.

10. The Wild honored the Minnesota North Stars franchise on April 4, 2017, by wearing North Stars' sweaters during the team's pre-game warm-up. Of course, the North Stars were the first NHL franchise in Minnesota. It move to Dallas in 1993 and the name was shortened to "Stars."

CHAPTER 3:

FAMOUS QUOTES

QUIZ TIME!

1. Which former Wild coach said this about meeting with the general manager and getting fired: "As soon as he shut the door, I knew "?

    a. Mike Yeo
    b. John Torchetti
    c. Bruce Boudreau
    d. Todd Richards

2. Who did this quote originate from: "We've got to try to find more ugly goals out there"?

    a. Devan Dubnyk
    b. Nicklas Bäckström
    c. Marián Gáborík
    d. Andrew Brunette

3. Eric Belanger said, "Sometimes you do the hard work and set the table and somebody else eats the meal."

    a. True
    b. False

4. "Every year I just want to do better than the year before," was said by which player?

   a. Zach Parise
   b. Ryan Suter
   c. Jonas Brodin
   d. Jared Spurgeon

5. Who commented, "Everybody wants to come back and play. We wanted that from the second it got stopped," when the 2019-20 season was paused due to Covid-19?

   a. Devan Dubnyk
   b. Kevin Fiala
   c. Marcus Foligno
   d. Matt Dumba

6. "I'm happy with my decision and I'm happy where I am right now" was said by which player after he signed a multi-year deal with Minnesota as a free agent?

   a. Zach Parise
   b. Ryan Suter
   c. Brian Rolston
   d. Eric Staal

7. When speaking about free agents, which general manager remarked, "Whatever is going to improve this organization going forward to give us a chance to win the Stanley Cup, we're going to look at "?

   a. Bill Guerin
   b. Chuck Fletcher

c. Paul Fenton

d. Doug Risebrough

8. When discussing his squad's road struggles former coach Jacques Lemaire once stated, "We play better at home and we need to find that intensity on the road."

a. True

b. False

9. Which player said this in 2018: "My wife and I have lived here for the last 10 or 11 years, went to school here and I'm just excited the Wild has given me an opportunity "?

a. Pontus Aberg

b. Matt Read

c. Louis Delpedio

d. Jordan Greenway

10. Who said this about forward Jason Zucker in 2018: "We see Jason as being a big part of both now and the future"?

a. Eric Fehr

b. Mikael Granlund

c. General Manager Paul Fenton

d. Victor Rask

11. Jim Dowd once made this optimistic comment about the Wild's playoff hopes: "Look at the bright side. We only got one point, but we're tied for first place with Calgary."

a. True

b. False

12. Which Wild player said this about his performance in the 2019-20 regular season: "In terms of individual play, it has not been the best in my view"?

    a. Luke Kunin
    b. Mats Zuccarello
    c. Ryan Hartman
    d. Alex Stalock

13. "He looks like he's having fun playing hockey." Which forward was head coach Dean Evason referring to when he said this in 2020?

    a. Alexander Galchenyuk
    b. Nico Sturm
    c. Mikko Koivu
    d. Kevin Fiala

14. Coach Mike Yeo said this about the club's poor start in 2009-10: "When I do go to sleep, I find myself crying like a baby."

    a. True
    b. False

15. Which veteran once said, "I totally understand when younger guys beat me out for ice time"?

    a. Matt Hendricks
    b. Keith Carney
    c. Matt Cullen
    d. Willie Mitchell

16. Which former Minnesota skater once said this about training camp: "By that time the wife doesn't like you that much anyway, so it's good to get out"?

    a. Dany Heatley
    b. Owen Nolan
    c. Brent Burns
    d. Todd White

17. "If I would be a healthy scratch, if it helped the team, that's good. I will not cry" was the opinion of which player?

    a. Marek Zidlicky
    b. Martin Skoula
    c. Joel Ward
    d. Dwayne Roloson

18. Which member of the Wild remarked, "It is what it is. There are way worse things that happen in the world than just us stopping playing hockey," when the 2019-20 season was suspended?

    a. General Manager Bill Guerin
    b. Joel Eriksson Eke
    c. Jared Spurgeon
    d. Alexander Galchenyuk

19. "I'm not satisfied with what I did last year and I'm excited to keep working this summer and get back at it," was said by whom before the 2018-19 campaign?

    a. J.T. Brown
    b. Charlie Coyle

c. Anthony Bitetto

d. Jason Zucker

20. Jason Zucker criticized general manager Bill Guerin by saying the following after a loss: "I think we need more than a meeting to jump-start us, to be honest with you."

a. True

b. False

QUIZ ANSWERS

1. C – Bruce Boudreau

2. C – Marián Gáborík

3. B – False

4. A – Zach Parise

5. A – Devan Dubnyk

6. B – Ryan Suter

7. C – Paul Fenton

8. A – True

9. B – Matt Read

10. C – General Manager Paul Fenton

11. A – True

12. D – Alex Stalock

13. A – Alexander Galchenyuk

14. B – False

15. A – Matt Hendricks

16. C – Brent Burns

17. A – Marek Zidlicky

18. D – Alexander Galchenyuk

19. D – Jason Zucker

20. B-False

DID YOU KNOW?

1. The Wild were beaten by Chicago in six games in the 2013-14 playoffs and then faced them again the next year. Minnesota downed the Central Division champions, the St. Louis Blues, in six games in the first round and believed they would be able to handle Chicago. However, they were swept in four straight. Following the stunning defeat, Wild forward Matt Cooke said, "Our expectations inside this room were a lot higher than a second-round series."

2. After being fired in 2020, former Wild head coach Bruce Boudreau remarked, "This is our home. I think more than any other team — I thought I dove in pretty good everywhere I went, but I think I delved in more here. Anything anybody asked I did because I just loved this franchise and these fans. It was always pro-Wild, whether it was doing the State Fair appearances or charitable endeavors or doing radio and TV."

3. Former Wild star Marián Gáborík had this to say about adjusting to playing in the NHL: "I was used to not having to check the defensive zone. I had to learn to adjust to it, otherwise I was going to be in the minors."

4. When the Wild were set to miss the playoffs in the team's first season, Gáborík said, "We want to finish strong and get some wins. Some guys are battling for jobs and stuff,

obviously. You want to end things on a good note for the fans. They've supported us the whole time, so we want to finish the best we can."

5. Zach Parise's father played with the Minnesota North Stars and Parise reminisced about growing up as a hockey family by commenting, "I don't remember life before hockey, driving to the rink while it was still dark out or skating on the pond after school until dinnertime. And now I see it with my son. I get teary-eyed watching him skate, and I'm sure it was the same for my dad watching me when I was young."

6. During a hot streak, goaltender Devan Dubnyk explained the feeling by remarking, "You learn to win in every different kind of way and every different kind of situation. We've been doing that through this run here, and it just makes you feel like going into every game like you can win every game. That's a fun way to play hockey."

7. When the 2019-20 season was first postponed due to the Covid-19 pandemic and talk of playing in hub cities was mentioned, Dubnyk told the media, "Guys with kids at home aren't interested in shacking up somewhere for four months and being away from them. I know myself personally, I'm not interested in packing up and going away for that length of time away from my family."

8. Blue-liner Ryan Suter said this about representing his homeland in international hockey. "I feel it's an honor to wear the Team USA Jersey and every time I'm on the ice I

play my hardest and give everything I have. When I got the call and was asked to play on this team, it was an easy answer. It didn't matter who was on the team or who the coach was. It's just an honor to wear the jersey and compete for your country. "

9. Former Wild player Matt Read was born in Canada but went to college in Minnesota, then decided to live there full-time. After signing with the team as a free agent in 2018, he said, "I brag about how beautiful the summers are. I love it here. Everything is great; great golf, great fishing, just a great spot to live. I'm excited to live at home this year."

10. Former general manager Paul Fenton had this to say about Jason Zucker after signing him to a five-year-27.5 million contract extension in 2018: "When we look at the league now, we look at the speed that has started to dominate our game. He generates so many chances based off of his speed and skill level. It's really hard to find natural goal scorers, and he's had a history of being able to score goals."

CHAPTER 4:

CATCHY NICKNAMES

QUIZ TIME!

1. What do Mats Zuccarello's teammates call him?

   a. Zucc

   b. Zuzu

   c. Sleeper

   d. Sizzle

2. By what nickname did Jared Spurgeon call former teammate Tyler Ennis?

   a. Ennis the Menace

   b. Mr. T

   c. Uncle Rico

   d. Patches

3. Devan Dubnyk is called "Dubey."

   a. True

   b. False

4. What nickname did Nicklas Bäckström have written on his mask while he played for the Wild?

   a. Nickel
   b. Brick
   c. Nikke
   d. Backs

5. Which Wild player was known as "Ace?"

   a. Marián Gáborík
   b. Brent Burns
   c. Kim Johnson
   d. Eric Belanger

6. Who marked his sticks with "Grumpy 21" instead of their actual name?

   a. Ryan White
   b. Cam Stewart
   c. Mark Parrish
   d. Eric Fehr

7. What do Matt Dumba's teammates call him?

   a. Dumbo
   b. Drummer
   c. Dumbs
   d. El Tigre

8. Mikko Koivu is known as "Captain K."

   a. True
   b. False

9. Who is known as "Moose"?

    a. Carson Soucy
    b. Victor Rask
    c. Brad Hunt
    d. Marcus Foligno

10. What superhero nickname did Christian Folin get while in Minnesota?

    a. Thor
    b. Batman
    c. Flash
    d. Superman

11. Todd Fedoruk was known as the fridge because of his size, standing at 6' 2" tall.

    a. True
    b. False

12. Who was known as "the Mayor?"

    a. Gustav Olofsson
    b. Jason Pominville
    c. Mike Reilly
    d. Mikael Granlund

13. What was Branko Radivojevic's moniker?

    a. Brad
    b. Banker
    c. Radio
    d. Branksey

14. In Slovakia, Marián Gáborík is nicknamed "Brambor," which means "potato."

    a. True
    b. False

15. Which was not one of Benoit Pouliot's nicknames?

    a. Pouly
    b. Pouls
    c. Benny
    d. Poultry

16. Who is nicknamed "Easy E"?

    a. Ryan Hartman
    b. Joel Eriksson Ek
    c. Nico Sturm
    d. Jonas Brodin

17. What was Dwayne Roloson commonly known as during his career?

    a. Rolo
    b. The Wall
    c. The Doctor
    d. Rolie the Goalie

18. Stéphane Veilleux was nicknamed after which food because of his red hair?

    a. Orange
    b. Peach
    c. Carrot
    d. Pumpkin

19. Which player was known as the "Designated Checker"?

   a. Wes Walz

   b. Filip Kuba

   c. Richard Park

   d. Andrew Brunette

20. Mike Rupp was called, "The Grim Rupper" by Minnesota teammates.

   a. True

   b. False

QUIZ ANSWERS

1. A – Zucc

2. C – Uncle Rico

3. A – True

4. D – Backs

5. B – Brent Burns

6. C – Mark Parrish

7. C – Dumbs

8. B – False

9. D – Marcus Foligno

10. A – Thor

11. A – True

12. B – Jason Pominville

13. C – Radio

14. A – True

15. D – Poultry

16. B – Joel Eriksson Ek

17. D – Rolie the Goalie

18. C – Carrot

19. A – Wes Walz

20. B – False

DID YOU KNOW?

1. St. Paul and Minneapolis are commonly known as "The Twin Cities" because they adjoin each other. St. Paul is also sometimes referred to as "the Capital City," "Pig's Eye," "Last City of the East," "STP," and "The Saintly City." The state of Minnesota is generally known as "Land of 10,000 Lakes," "North Star State," "The Gopher State," "True North," "Agate State," and "the State of Hockey." With the Wild being such a short name already, the hockey club isn't commonly known by any nickname. However, some have referred to the team as "Minny," "Brisket Bonanza," "ManBearPigs," and "The Mild."

2. Former head coach Bruce Boudreau was given the moniker "Gabby" during his playing days due to his penchant for talking. He even released a book titled *"Gabby: Confessions of a Hockey Lifer."* Boudreau was behind the Wild bench for almost four full seasons beginning in 2016-17. As a player, he posted 70 points in 140 NHL games and 995 points in 779 minor league outings.

3. Another Wild player who was nicknamed "Gabs" and "Gabby" by his teammates was Marián Gáborík. However, in his homeland of Slovakia, Gáborík was given the moniker "Brambor," which means potato. Gáborík said his older brother is named Brano and he was nicknamed Brambor and the name was eventually passed down to Marián.

4. Blue-liner Matt Barkowski signed as a free agent with Minnesota in the summer of 2018 after leaving the Calgary Flames. Most fans know him by his nickname of "Tank Commander." Barkowski had posted 48 points in 255 regular-season games by the end of the 2019-20 regular season but had played just two games with the Wild.

5. Former enforcer Derek Boogaard was known as "The Boogie Man" during his playing days. Boogaard skated on the wing with Minnesota from 2005 to 2010 and earned 544 penalty minutes in 255 regular-season outings. Boogaard suffered several injuries during his career and unfortunately passed away in May of 2011 at the age of 28 while a member of the New York Rangers.

6. Forward Chris Simon was another enforcer-type player for the team. He finished his career in Minnesota in 2007-08. Simon says when he first arrived at the Wild, Brent Burns asked him his nickname. Simon replied that he was known as "Si" or "Chief" because of his native Canadian background. Burns then asked "Wolf?" and many of his teammates started calling him by his new moniker.

7. Charlie Coyle was one of many NHL players who has several nicknames. He was known typically by the following; "Baby Gronk," "Sir Charles," "Mayor of Weymouth," and "Chowdah." Most of the monikers deal with the fact that Coyle was born in Weymouth, Massachusetts, near Boston. Coyle played with the Wild from 2012-13 to 2018-19.

8. Matt Cooke was known by many as "Cookie" and "The Cookie Monster." He played over 1,000 NHL games, won the Stanley Cup with Pittsburgh, and was a supreme agitator. Cooke was suspended several times by the league, including a seven-game ban while playing with the Wild in the 2014 playoffs. He joined Minnesota in 2013 and was placed on waivers in June 2015 for the purpose of buying out his contract.

9. Forward Pierre-Marc Bouchard was naturally known as "Butch" by his teammates. This was in honor of legendary Montreal Canadiens' blue-liner and Hall of Famer Emile "Butch" Bouchard and his son Pierre "Butch" Bouchard, who also played for the Canadiens. Pierre-Marc played with the Wild from 2002 to 2013.

10. Hockey players are often known for their drab nicknames. A prime example is defender Keith Carney simply being called "Carnes." However, he was also known as "Art" Carney by some in honor of the actor who played Ed Norton on the famous *Honeymooners* television series with Jackie Gleason. Carney, who played with the Wild from 2006 to 2008, said he was called Art in his early days and it followed him to Minnesota, where his former Buffalo teammate Mike Ramsey was an assistant coach.

CHAPTER 5:

THE CAPTAIN CLASS

QUIZ TIME!

1. How many different players served as a captain for the Wild from 2000 to 2020?

   a. 8

   b. 10

   c. 17

   d. 22

2. Who has been the team's captain since 2009?

   a. Jared Spurgeon

   b. Eric Staal

   c. Mikko Koivu

   d. Ryan Suter

3. Until 2009, the Wild would generally rotate the captaincy each month in a season.

   a. True

   b. False

4. How many captains did the club have in 2007-08?

    a. 2
    b. 4
    c. 5
    d. 3

5. Which captain scored the most goals in a season?

    a. Owen Nolan
    b. Marián Gáborík
    c. Brian Rolston
    d. Mark Parrish

6. Who was captain in December 2000-01?

    a. Darby Hendrickson
    b. Scott Pellerin
    c. Sean O'Donnell
    d. Wes Walz

7. This player was not captain in 2002-03.

    a. Matt Johnson
    b. Brad Bombardir
    c. Andrew Brunette
    d. Sergei Zholtok

8. The most penalty minutes recorded by a captain in a season is 201.

    a. True
    b. False

9. Which player served as co-captain with Mikko Koivu in 2008-09?

   a. Owen Nolan
   b. Andrew Brunette
   c. Willie Mitchel
   d. Brad Brown

10. What is the most assists recorded in a season by a captain?

   a. 47
   b. 49
   c. 46
   d. 50

11. Mikko Koivu posted the most points in a season for a captain.

   a. True
   b. False

12. Which player did not serve as captain when he was 25 years old?

   a. Mikko Koivu
   b. Filip Kuba
   c. Nick Schultz
   d. Jim Dowd

13. Which captain scored 39 points in the 2007-08 season?

   a. Brian Rolston
   b. Nick Schultz
   c. Pavol Demitra
   d. Mark Parrish

14. Jim Dowd was the oldest serving captain at the age of 37.

    a. True

    b. False

15. How many goals did Richard Park score in 2003-04?

    a. 13

    b. 17

    c. 12

    d. 15

16. Who had a +22 rating in 2006-07?

    a. Keith Carney

    b. Willie Mitchel

    c. Pavol Demitra

    d. Alex Henry

17. Which captain scored 42 points in 2002-03?

    a. Sean O'Donnell

    b. Matt Johnson

    c. Sergei Zholtok

    d. Andrew Brunette

18. How many players served as captain in the club's inaugural season?

    a. 2

    b. 3

    c. 4

    d. 5

19. These two players have served as alternate captains from 2012-13 through the 2019-20 season.

    a. Jason Zucker and Zach Parise
    b. Zach Parise and Ryan Suter
    c. Gabriel Dumont and Jason Zucker
    d. Jared Spurgeon and Ryan Suter

20. Brad Brown scored a total of 5 points in the two seasons in which he served as captain.

    a. True
    b. False

QUIZ ANSWERS

1. D – 22

2. C – Mikko Koivu

3. A – True

4. C – 5

5. B – Marián Gáborík

6. D – Wes Walz

7. C – Andrew Brunette

8. A – True

9. A – Owen Nolan

10. B – 49

11. B – False

12. D – Jim Dowd

13. C – Pavol Demitra

14. B – False

15. A – 13

16. A – Keith Carney

17. C – Sergei Zholtok

18. D – 5

19. B – Zach Parise and Ryan Suter

20. A – True

DID YOU KNOW?

1. The Wild had a somewhat confusing system of rotating the team captaincy every month or two during their first nine seasons in the NHL. This meant several players acted as captain on more than one occasion under head coach Jacques Lemaire.

2. When Todd Richards took over as head coach for the 2009-10 season, he named Mikko Koivu as the lone captain of the squad. Koivu had worn the "C" on his sweater for the first time in the previous season when he split the duties with fellow forward Owen Nolan. Koivu was handed the job on Oct. 20, 2009, and was still captain in 2019-20.

3. Twenty-two different players have acted as the Wild captain at least once during their stint with the team. Here are the number of captains in each season: 2000-01 (5); 2001-02(4); 2002-03 (3), 2003-04 (5); 2004-05 (no NHL season); 2005-06 (5); 2006-07 (3); 2007-08 (5); 2008-09 (2); 2009-10 to 2019-20 (1).

4. The Wild prefers their captains to be somewhat experienced players, as four of them have been an acting captain when they were 25 years old; Mikko Koivu, Marián Gáborík, Nick Schultz, and Filip Kuba. The oldest players to skipper the squad have been Koivu, Owen Nolan, and Keith Carney, all of whom wore the "C" when they were 36 years old.

5. The most rambunctious captain so far was winger Matt Johnson, who wore the "C" in December 2002. He was acquired in September of 2000 in a trade with Atlanta. Johnson served 201 penalty minutes during the season he wore the "C" and accumulated 698 minutes in 227 games with the team. He also served 25 minutes in 12 playoff outings before his NHL career came to an end in 2004.

6. Veteran winger Owen Nolan was the last co-captain of the team before Mikko Koivu took over in 2009-10. Nolan and Koivu shared the duties in 2008-09. Nolan was a former first-overall draft pick in 1990 when the Quebec Nordiques took him. He signed as a free agent in July 2008 and played his last two NHL seasons with the Wild. Nolan notched 78 points in 132 games with the club.

7. Marián Gáborík enjoyed the most productive campaign with the team when wearing the C. He racked up 42 goals and 41 assists for 83 points in 2007-08 and was acting captain in March and April 2008. Brian Rolston wasn't too far behind, as he posted 34 goals and 45 assists for 79 points in 2005-06.

8. When the Wild joined the league in 2000, defender Sean O'Donnell was the acting captain in October. The Wild claimed him from Los Angeles in the June 2000 NHL expansion draft. O'Donnell was traded before the team's first season was over as he went to New Jersey for rearguard Willie Mitchell in March 2001 after posting 16 points in 63 games with 128 penalty minutes.

9. Willie Mitchell, who was acquired for Sean O'Donnell, acted as captain a few years later, as he wore the "C" in December 2005 and January 2006. Mitchell played 288 regular-season contests with Minnesota and tallied 57 points and 333 penalty minutes. He was then traded to Dallas in March 2006.

10. The 22 players who have acted as Wild captain since the team joined the league are Sean O'Donnell, Scott Pellerin, Wes Walz, Brad Bombardir, Darby Hendrickson, Jim Dowd, Filip Kuba, Brad Brown, Andrew Brunette, Matt Johnson, Sergei Zholtok, Richard Park, Alex Henry, Willie Mitchell, Brian Rolston, Keith Carney, Mark Parrish, Pavol Demitra, Nick Schultz, Marián Gáborík,Owen Nolan, and Mikko Koivu.

CHAPTER 6:

STATISTICALLY SPEAKING

QUIZ TIME!

1. What is the most goals scored in a season by a Wild player?

    a. 38
    b. 42
    c. 33
    d. 46

2. Which player leads the team with 698 penalty minutes?

    a. Brent Burns
    b. Cal Clutterbuck
    c. Matt Johnson
    d. Derek Boogaard

3. Mikko Koivu has played over 1,000 NHL games.

    a. True
    b. False

4. What is the most hat tricks scored by one player in a regular season as of 2019-20?

    a. 3
    b. 4
    c. 5
    d. 6

5. What is the most games a Minnesota goalie has played in a season?

    a. 60
    b. 65
    c. 67
    d. 71

6. Who scored 15 power-play goals in one season, the most in franchise history?

    a. Eric Staal
    b. Andrew Brunette
    c. Brian Rolston
    d. Owen Nolan

7. How any career goals did Marián Gáborík score with the Wild?

    a. 219
    b. 198
    c. 207
    d. 223

8. Four players are tied for scoring the most game-winning goals in a season.

a. True

b. False

9. Who scored the most short-handed goals in a season as of 2019-20?

   a. Jason Zucker

   b. Matt Cullen

   c. Wes Walz

   d. Brian Rolston

10. How many regular-season wins did coach Jacques Lemaire have in Minnesota?

    a. 255

    b. 289

    c. 173

    d. 293

11. Eric Staal averaged the most points per game in a Wild season with 1.19.

    a. True

    b. False

12. Which Wild goalie has made the most saves in a season as of 2019-20?

    a. Devan Dubnyk

    b. Nicklas Bäckström

    c. Dwayne Roloson

    d. Manny Fernandez

13. Who leads the club in career points?

    a. Marián Gáborík
    b. Ryan Suter
    c. Mikko Koivu
    d. Pierre-Marc Bouchard

14. Pierre-Marc Bouchard earned the most assists in franchise history in the 2007-08 season.

    a. True
    b. False

15. Brian Rolston has the most shots on net in a season with how many?

    a. 280
    b. 289
    c. 293
    d. 305

16. Who averaged 0.60 assists per game in 2017-18?

    a. Mikael Granlund
    b. Jason Zucker
    c. Eric Staal
    d. Matt Dumba

17. Which goaltender had 11 ties/overtime losses as of 2019-20?

    a. Jamie McLennan
    b. Dwayne Roloson
    c. Manny Fernandez
    d. Jose Theodore

18. What was Guillaume Latendresse's goals per game average in 2009-10?

    a. 0.51
    b. 0.38
    c. 0.43
    d. 0.45

19. How many seasons have the Wild posted 100 or more points?

    a. 2
    b. 1
    c. 4
    d. 3

20. Jamie McLennan has the most losses by a goalie in a season.

    a. True
    b. False

QUIZ ANSWERS

1. B – 42

2. C – Matt Johnson

3. A – True

4. A – 3

5. D – 71

6. C – Brian Rolston

7. A – 219

8. B – False

9. A – Wes Walz

10. D – 293

11. B – False

12. B – Nicklas Bäckström

13. C – Mikko Koivu

14. A – True

15. D – 305

16. A – Mikael Granlund

17. B – Dwayne Roloson

18. D – 0.45

19. C – 4

20. B – False

DID YOU KNOW?

1. When the 2019-20 NHL regular season officially came to an end, the Wild had an all-time (won-lost-tied-overtime/shootout losses) record of 724-583-55-149 for 1,652 points and were 26-47 in the playoffs at the conclusion of the 2018-19 postseason.

2. The most points the Wild earned in a season was the 106 they posted in the 2017-18 campaign, with a record of 49-25-8. The fewest points was 55 in 2012-13, with a mark of 26-19-3 in the shortened 48-game season. The fewest points the squad earned in an 82-game season was 68 in their first NHL campaign at 25-39-18.

3. As of 2019-20, Marián Gáborík holds several career franchise records, including the most goals (219), even-strength goals (154), game-winning goals (43), hat tricks (9), goals per game (0.44), and points per game (0.87). He also holds several single-season records: most points in a season (83), even-strength goals (30), goals per game (0.63), and points per game (1.19). He shares the record for most goals in a season at 42 with Eric Staal and most game-winning goals at 8 with Eric Staal and Brian Rolston.

4. In some other all-time career highs, Mikko Koivu was leading in games played at the end of the 2019-20 regular season (1,028), as well as in assists (504), points (709), and plus/minus rating (+70). He also posted a team-best assists per game in a season (0.66).

5. Other team leaders for single-season records include Pierre-Marc Bouchard for assists in a season (50), Brian Rolston for most power-play goals (15) and shots on net (305), Wes Walz for most short-handed goals (7), Andrew Brunette for shooting percentage (19.8) and Matt Johnson for penalty minutes (201). Johnson also holds the all-time high for 698 career penalty minutes.

6. In goaltending single-season records, Nicklas Bäckström played the most games (71), faced the most shots (2,059), made the most saves (1,900), played the most minutes (4,088), and posted the most shutouts (8). Devan Dubnyk has the most wins (40), most losses (28), most goals against (163), best save percentage (.936), and best goals-against average with at least 25 games played (1.78).

7. Career regular-season goaltending records are held by Nicklas Bäckström for games played (409), wins (194), losses (142), ties/overtime/shootout losses (50), goals against (962), shots against (11,283), saves (10,321), minutes (23,248) and shutouts (28). Dwayne Roloson owns the best save career percentage (.919) and best goals-against average with a minimum of 100 games played (2.28).

8. The most points by a Wild blue-liner in a season was set by Ryan Suter (51), Marián Gáborík holds the records for most points by a rookie (36) and most goals in a game (5). Zach Parise scored the fastest hat trick (11:12) and has scored the most career power-play goals (69), Wes Walz has tallied the most career short-handed markers (14), and

Parise and Suter share the best plus-minus rating in a season at +34.

9. In the playoffs, Marián Gáborík holds the single-season Wild records for goals (9) and points (17). Sergei Zholtok posted the most assists (11) while Stéphane Veilleux was assessed the most penalty minutes (27) and goaltender Dwayne Roloson won the most games (5).

10. In career postseason records for the Wild, Mikko Koivu has played the most games (55), Zach Parise scored the most goals (14) and points (31) and shares the mark for most assists with Mikko Koivu (17). Derek Boogaard racked up the most penalty minutes (44). Devan Dubnyk played the most games in goal (26) won the most (8), lost the most (18), and posted 2 shutouts. Manny Fernandez posted the best goals-against average in a minimum of nine games (1.96) and the best save percentage (.929).

CHAPTER 7:

THE TRADE MARKET

QUIZ TIME!

1. Who was the first player the Wild acquired by trade, on June 11, 2000?

    a. Andy Sutton

    b. Manny Fernandez

    c. Brad Lukowich

    d. Brad Bombardir

2. In 2013, the Wild traded Cal Clutterbuck and a third-round draft pick for which rookie forward?

    a. Jason Zucker

    b. Charlie Coyle

    c. Mikael Granlund

    d. Nino Niederreiter

3. The Wild made 13 trades in the 2011-12 season.

    a. True

    b. False

4. What did the Wild trade to the Arizona Coyotes to acquire Devan Dubnyk in 2015?

    a. Nicklas Bäckström and a 2016 3rd-round draft pick
    b. 2015 2nd and 3rd -round picks
    c. Justin Falk and a 2015 5th-round pick
    d. A 2015 3rd-round pick

5. Who did Minnesota receive from Chicago for Kim Johnsson and Nick Leddy?

    a. Aaron Johnson
    b. Daryl Boyle
    c. Cam Barker
    d. Joe Fallon

6. Which two players did Minnesota trade to Buffalo for Tyler Ennis and Marcus Foligno?

    a. Mario Lucia and Jason Pominville
    b. Mikael Granlund and Marco Scandella
    c. Christoph Bertschy and Mario Lucia
    d. Marco Scandella and Jason Pominville

7. Which team did the Wild acquire Dominic Moore from in 2006-07?

    a. Pittsburgh Penguins
    b. Toronto Maple Leafs
    c. New York Rangers
    d. Buffalo Sabres

8. Minnesota traded Brent Burns and a 2012 2nd-round draft pick for Devin Setoguchi, Charlie Coyle, and a 2011 1st-round pick.

a. True

b. False

9. How many trades did Minnesota make in 2014-15?

    a. 10

    b. 5

    c. 9

    d. 7

10. On July 3, 2011, the Wild traded Martin Havlat for which veteran forward?

    a. David McIntyre

    b. Mike Rupp

    c. Dany Heatley

    d. Erik Christensen

11. Minnesota traded Charlie Coyle to the Nashville Predators for Kevin Fiala.

    a. True

    b. False

12. The Wild acquired forward Kyle Brodziak from Edmonton in exchange for what?

    a. Eric Belanger and a 2009 4th-round draft pick

    b. Benoit Pouliot

    c. A 2009 3rd-round draft pick

    d. 2009 4th and 5th-round draft picks

13. From what team did Minnesota acquire Pavol Demitra in 2006-07?

a. Ottawa Senators

b. Vancouver Canucks

c. Los Angeles Kings

d. St. Louis Blues

14. In January 2019, the Wild traded Nino Niederreiter for Victor Rask.

a. True

b. False

15. The Wild traded Pascal Dupuis for which short-term rental?

a. Adam Hall

b. Aaron Voros

c. Petteri Nummelin

d. Petr Kalus

16. What trade package did the Wild send to the Arizona Coyotes for Martin Hanzal and Ian White?

a. Grayson Downing and three future draft picks

b. Teemu Pulkkinen, Grayson Downing, and a 2018 2nd-round draft pick

c. 1st- and 2nd -round draft picks

d. Grayson Downing and a 2018 1st-round draft pick

17. To which team did the Wild trade goalie Dwayne Roloson to for a 2006 1st-round and a 2007 3rd-round draft pick?

a. Calgary Flames

b. Tampa Bay Lightning

c. New York Islanders

d. Edmonton Oilers

18. Which of these players was not involved in a trade with the Buffalo Sabres on March 14, 2014?

    a. Torrey Mitchell
    b. Cody McCormick
    c. Benn Ferriero
    d. Matt Moulson

19. Which player did Minnesota trade to the Vegas Golden Knights before the expansion draft for a 2018 3rd-round draft pick?

    a. Mike Reilly
    b. Alex Tuch
    c. Tyler Graovac
    d. Jordan Schroeder

20. Minnesota traded goalie Anton Khudobin for two young prospects who never played an NHL game for the Wild.

    a. True
    b. False

QUIZ ANSWERS

1. A – Andy Sutton

2. D – Nino Niederreiter

3. B – False

4. D – A 2015 3rd-round pick

5. C – Cam Barker

6. D – Marco Scandella and Jason Pominville

7. A – Pittsburgh Penguins

8. A – True

9. B – 5

10. C – Dany Heatley

11. B – False

12. D – 2009 4th- and 5th-round draft picks

13. C – Los Angeles Kings

14. A – True

15. A – Adam Hall

16. A – Grayson Downing and three future draft picks

17. D – Edmonton Oilers

18. C – Benn Ferriero

19. B – Alex Tuch

20. A – True

DID YOU KNOW?

1. In the first trade the franchise was involved in, the Wild acquired defenseman Andy Sutton from San Jose in June 2000. They also received a seventh-round draft pick in 2000 and a third-round draft pick in 2001. Going to San Jose was an eighth-round draft pick and future considerations. Sutton didn't last long in Minnesota, though, as he was traded to Atlanta in January 2002 after 88 regular-season games for Hnat Domenichelli.

2. The worst trade the Wild ever made in most fans' eyes saw Brent Burns and a 2012 second-round draft pick head to San Jose in June 2011 for Devin Setoguchi, Charlie Coyle, and a 2011 first-round pick. Burns was drafted 20th overall by the Wild in 2003 as a forward and then was converted to a rearguard. He suffered several injuries in Minnesota but posted 183 points in 453 games. He's tallied 511 points in 660 outings with San Jose as of the conclusion of the 2019-20 season, added 59 points in 83 playoff contests, is a three-time All-Star, and won the James Norris Trophy in 2016-17.

3. The Wild made another big trade with San Jose in the summer of 2011 when they acquired 31-year-old Dany Heatley, who was drafted second overall by Atlanta in 2000. In doing so, they gave up fellow winger Martin Havlat, who had scored 116 points in 151 games with

Minnesota. Havlat played another 169 regular-season NHL games with 82 points, while Heatley posted 102 points in 194 outings with the Wild with six points in 11 playoff games.

4. Ryan Donato arrived in a trade with Boston in February 2019 which saw fellow center Charlie Coyle go the other way and Minnesota also pick up a fifth-round draft pick. Donato just turned 24 years old in 2020 and looks to have a promising future. He posted 39 points in his first 84 regular-season games with the club while averaging 11.55 minutes of ice time per game. Coyle was a solid player for the Wild but had just one 20-goal season while posting 242 points in 479 regular-season games.

5. Minnesota acquired goaltender Devan Dubnyk from Arizona in January 2015 for a third-round draft pick to push fellow netminders Darcy Kuemper and Nicklas Bäckström, both of whom were struggling at the time. After arriving in Minnesota, Dubnyk started a club-record 38 consecutive games and posted a 1.78 goals-against average with a .936 save percentage as he earned 27 wins to help the team reach the second round of the playoffs. Dubnyk has turned out to be one of the most consistent netminders in the NHL. At the end of the 2019-20 regular season, he had a 177-113-28 record with the Wild, with a 2.41 goals-against average and a .918 save percentage.

6. The Wild gave up winger Ryan Jones and a second-round draft pick to Nashville in July 2008 and received defender Marek Zidlicky in return. Jones was drafted 111th by

Minnesota in 2004 but never played a game for the club before being traded. He went on to play 334 regular-season NHL games, compiling 100 points, while Zidlicky posted 123 points in 243 outings with the Wild. He was then traded to New Jersey in February 2012 in a multi-player deal.

7. With 110 goals and 228 points in 434 regular-season contests with Minnesota, Nino Niederreiter was a pretty good pickup. The Wild acquired him and a third-round draft pick for fellow forward Cal Clutterbuck in June 2013. Clutterbuck had scored 110 points in 346 games with the Wild. However, Minnesota then traded Niederreiter to Carolina in January 2019 for center Victor Rask, who managed just 16 points in his first 66 games with the Wild by the end of the 2019-20 regular season.

8. Goaltender Dwayne Roloson signed as a free agent with the Wild in July 2001 and went on to post a 62-71-27 mark in 167 regular-season matches with a fine 2.28 goals-against average and .919 save percentage. The Wild traded Roloson to Edmonton in March 2006 for a first-round draft pick. They later traded the draft pick to Los Angeles along with Patrick O'Sullivan for forward Pavol Demitra.

9. Pavol Demitra arrived in Minnesota in June 2006 and the forward went on to play 139 games with the team, notching 40 goals and 118 points, with 7 points in 11 playoff contests. Demitra, who won the Lady Byng Trophy in 1999-2000, then signed as a free agent with Vancouver in July 2008. Sadly, Demitra lost his life in September 2011

at the age of 36 when his KHL club, Lokomotiv Yaroslavl, was involved in a tragic plane crash in Russia.

10. In June 2007, the Wild traded first- and second-round draft picks to Anaheim for the Ducks' first-round selection. This enabled Minnesota to move up in the 2007 draft from the 19th to the 16th spot. Both teams missed the boat though, as the Wild chose winger Colton Gillies, who would post 18 points in 154 NHL games, while Anaheim drafted Logan MacMillan and Eric Tangradi. MacMillan never played in the NHL and Tangradi notched 16 points in 150 career outings. Minnesota and Anaheim both passed over Max Pacioretty and David Perron.

CHAPTER 8:

DRAFT DAY

QUIZ TIME!

1. Who was Minnesota's first-ever draft pick?

    a. Nick Schultz

    b. Ľubomír Sekeráš

    c. Marián Gáborík

    d. Mikko Koivu

2. How many players has Minnesota drafted as of 2019?

    a. 152

    b. 137

    c. 150

    d. 145

3. The Wild has drafted 39 centers as of 2019.

    a. True

    b. False

4. Who did the Wild draft 72nd overall in 2006?

    a. Cal Clutterbuck

    b. James Sheppard

    c. Justin Falk

    d. Benoit Pouliot

5. What year did the club draft Brent Burns?

    a. 2002

    b. 2004

    c. 2003

    d. 2005

6. In which round did the Wild select Jason Zucker during the 2010 draft?

    a. 1st

    b. 2nd

    c. 3rd

    d. 4th

7. How many first-round draft picks have the Wild made as of 2019?

    a. 14

    b. 22

    c. 7

    d. 19

8. In 2004, the Wild drafted 14 players.

    a. True

    b. False

9. This player was drafted 9th overall in 2010.

    a. Erik Haula

    b. Nick Leddy

   c. Mikael Granlund

   d. Johan Larsson

10. How many of the seven players Minnesota drafted in 2001 were wingers?

   a. 2

   b. 6

   c. 3

   d. 5

11. Minnesota has not had a first-overall draft pick as of 2019.

   a. True

   b. False

12. Which goalie did the club draft in the 6th round in 2009?

   a. Darcy Kuemper

   b. Matt Hackett

   c. Johan Gustafsson

   d. Steve Michalek

13. How many players did the club draft in 2016?

   a. 3

   b. 4

   c. 5

   d. 6

14. Minnesota has drafted 38 defensemen as of 2019.

   a. True

   b. False

15. Who is the only player Minnesota drafted in 2008 to play more than 100 NHL games?

    a. Sean Lorenz
    b. Eero Elo
    c. Marco Scandella
    d. Tyler Cuma

16. Which player did the Wild select 206th overall in 2004?

    a. Clayton Stoner
    b. Anton Khudobin
    c. Ryan Jones
    d. Patrick Bordeleau

17. How many of the eight players Minnesota selected in 2000 played at least one NHL game?

    a. 6
    b. 5
    c. 8
    d. 7

18. Who did the club select 7th overall in 2012?

    a. Alex Tuch
    b. Gustav Olofsson
    c. Jonas Brodin
    d. Matt Dumba

19. How many players did Minnesota select in the 3rd round in 2018?

    a. 1
    b. 2

c. 3

d. 4

20. Brent Burns was the highest-drafted player by the Wild, taken third overall.

    a. True

    b. False

QUIZ ANSWERS

1. C – Marián Gáborík

2. D – 145

3. A – True

4. A – Cal Clutterbuck

5. C – 2003

6. B – 2nd

7. D – 19

8. B – False

9. C – Mikael Granlund

10. D – 5

11. A – True

12. A – Darcy Kuemper

13. B – 4

14. A – True

15. C – Marco Scandella

16. B – Anton Khudobin

17. A – 6

18. D – Matt Dumba

19. C – 3

20. B – False

DID YOU KNOW?

1. Of the 145 players selected by the Wild as of the 2019 NHL entry draft, none was taken with the first overall pick. The highest-drafted player in team history was winger Marián Gáborík, who went third overall in 2000. He was also the first player the Wild drafted. Gáborík played with Minnesota until joining the New York Rangers as a free agent in 2009. He scored 407 goals and 815 points in 1,035 NHL regular-season games with a +95 rating and 58 points in 84 postseason outings.

2. The Wild has had two top-five draft packs as of 2019 and eight selections in the top 10. All eight of these players played at least 394 games during their NHL careers. The highest-drafted player who didn't play an NHL game in his career was A.J. Thelen, a defender taken from Michigan State 12th overall in 2004.

3. Minnesota has fared quite well in the first round of the draft as just four of their first-round picks had yet to play an NHL game as of 2019-20. However, two of these players were drafted in the past three years and still have a chance to play in the league. Winger Mathew Boldy was taken 12th overall in 2019, while blue-liner Filip Johansson was chosen 24th overall in 2018.

4. There has been just one occasion as of 2019 when the Wild had two draft picks in the first round in the same year. The

club selected defenseman Jonas Brodin with the 10th overall pick in 2011 and took center Zack Philips with the 28th pick. Brodin is still with the team and had 146 points in 555 regular-season games with a +47 rating at the conclusion of the 2019-20 regular season, while Phillips has yet to play an NHL contest.

5. The highest-drafted goaltender in Wild history was Josh Harding, who was taken with the 38th overall pick in 2002. Harding played his entire NHL career with Minnesota from 2005-06 to 2013-14 before retiring due to multiple sclerosis. He posted a 60-59-11 record in 151 games with a 2.45 goals-against average and a .918 save percentage. He won the Bill Masterton Trophy for 2013-14, when led the league in save percentage in 2013-14 at .933 and in goals-against average at 1.66.

6. The lowest-drafted Wild goalie as of 2019 also carved out a fine NHL career for himself. Anton Khudobin was taken 206th overall in 2004. He played just six regular-season games with Minnesota before being traded to Boston in February 2011. Khudobin was an excellent prospect with four wins in Minnesota while posting a sparkling 1.39 goals-against average with a .955 save percentage. He went on to notch a 99-76-25 record in 218 regular-season NHL games with a .919 save percentage and 2.46 goals-against average.

7. The lowest-drafted skater to play in at least 200 NHL games was Ľubomír Sekeráš. The blue-liner was taken in the eighth round with the 232nd overall pick in 2000,

when he was already 31 years old. The native of Czechoslovakia cracked the Wild's lineup in their inaugural season and played three campaigns for the team, notching 69 points in 209 regular-season contests. Sekeráš signed with Dallas as a free agent in March 2004 and played the final four games of his NHL career there.

8. When the Wild entered the NHL with Columbus in 2000-01, each team was allowed to select unprotected players from each of the other NHL clubs. This was known as the 2000 NHL expansion draft. Minnesota selected four goaltenders, nine defensemen, and 13 forwards in this draft to stock their lineup.

9. The most productive player after being selected by the Wild in the 2000 NHL expansion draft was Filip Kuba. The defenseman, the eighth player taken by Minnesota, went on to play another 818 regular-season NHL games, recording 69 goals and 326 points. Kuba racked up 132 points in 357 regular-season outings with the Wild before signing as a free agent with Tampa in July 2006.

10. The Wild also acquired players in each of the 2000 and 2001 NHL waiver drafts. They selected wingers Zdeno Cíger from Nashville and Sylvain Blouin from Montreal in 2000 and chose center Sébastien Bordeleau from St. Louis in 2001. In addition, they lost goaltender Martin Brochu to Vancouver in the 2001 draft. Cíger never played a game with the Wild while Blouin and Bordeleau played a combined 100 regular-season games with 12 points between them.

CHAPTER 9:

GOALTENDER TIDBITS

QUIZ TIME!

1. Which former Wild netminder recorded 36 career penalty minutes with the team?

   a. Josh Harding

   b. Nicklas Bäckström

   c. Dwayne Roloson

   d. Manny Fernandez

2. How many saves did Nicklas Bäckström make in the 2008-09 season?

   a. 1,679

   b. 1,900

   c. 1,701

   d. 1,714

3. Eighteen different goalies have played at least one game for Minnesota.

   a. True

   b. False

4. How many goalies did Minnesota use in the 2010-11 season?

   a. 2
   b. 3
   c. 4
   d. 5

5. Which goalie had 98 goals scored against him in the club's inaugural season?

   a. Derek Gustafson
   b. Zac Bierk
   c. Jamie McLennan
   d. Manny Fernandez

6. What save percentage did Devan Dubnyk post in the 2014-15 season?

   a. .933
   b. .929
   c. .936
   d. .924

7. How many shots did Dwayne Roloson and Manny Fernandez face in the 2002-03 playoffs?

   a. 492
   b. 508
   c. 439
   d. 510

8. As of 2020, Devan Dubnyk has the most points among Minnesota goaltenders.

a. True

b. False

9. Who had a goals-against average of 3.13 in 2016-17?

  a. Devan Dubnyk

  b. Darcy Kuemper

  c. Alex Stalock

  d. John Curry

10. How many games did Josh Harding lose in 2009 -10?

  a. 8

  b. 15

  c. 6

  d. 12

11. In the shortened 2012-13 season, Minnesota backup goalies played a total of 12 games.

  a. True

  b. False

12. Alex Stalock made how many saves in the 2018-19 campaign?

  a. 285

  b. 716

  c. 472

  d. 525

13. What was Matt Hackett's save percentage in 2011-12?

  a. .910

  b. .912

c. .914

d. .922

14. Dwayne Roloson recorded 12 regular-season shutouts with the Wild.

    a. True
    b. False

15. How many games did Ilya Bryzgalov win in the 2013-14 season?

    a. 15
    b. 7
    c. 12
    d. 9

16. Which goaltender recorded a save percentage of .887 in 2014-15?

    a. Nicklas Bäckström
    b. John Curry
    c. Darcy Kuemper
    d. Ilya Bryzgalov

17. Who played just six career games with the Wild and won four of them?

    a. Wade Dubielewicz
    b. Dieter Kochan
    c. Anton Khudobin
    d. Derek Gustafson

18. How many games did Jamie McLennan win in his lone season with the team?

a. 4

b. 8

c. 10

d. 5

19. As of 2019-20, how many goalies have played fewer than 10 games for the club?

    a. 4

    b. 5

    c. 6

    d. 7

20. Nicklas Bäckström won 203 regular-season games with Minnesota.

    a. True

    b. False

QUIZ ANSWERS

1. D – Manny Fernandez

2. B – 1,900

3. A – True

4. B – 3

5. C – Jamie McLennan

6. C – .936

7. D – 510

8. A – True

9. B – Darcy Kuemper

10. D – 12

11. A – True

12. C – 472

13. D – .922

14. B – False

15. B – 7

16. A – Nicklas Bäckström

17. C – Anton Khudobin

18. D – 5

19. C – 6

20. B – False

DID YOU KNOW?

1. The Wild had used a total of 18 different goaltenders from joining the NHL through the conclusion of the 2019-20 regular season. Two of these netminders, Zac Bierk and Dieter Kochan, played just one regular-season game with the squad, while seven of them played fewer than 10 games.

2. Minnesota goalies haven't exactly been the greatest puck handlers over the years, as just eight of the 18 have recorded an assist. Devan Dubnyk leads the way with 5 points, followed by Nicklas Bäckström with 5, Manny Fernandez with 4, Alex Stalock with 3, Dwayne Roloson and Josh Harding with 2 each, and Darcy Kuemper and Jamie McLennan with 1 assist apiece.

3. Wild goalies haven't really lived up to the team's nickname yet, as they've been more mild than wild. When it comes to penalty minutes, Devan Dubnyk and Manny Fernandez each had 36 career regular-season penalty minutes as of the conclusion of the 2019-20 season. Dwayne Roloson served 26 minutes while Nicklas Bäckström had 22. Just six other goalies received at least 2 minutes and the other eight goalies were assessed none.

4. The Wild has used four goalies in a regular season on several occasions throughout the team's history. However, the most goaltenders to play at least two games in a

campaign has been five. That happened in 2013-14, when Josh Harding appeared in 29 games, Darcy Kuemper in 26, Nicklas Bäckström in 21, Ilya Bryzgalov in 12, and John Curry in 2.

5. When Manny Fernandez tended goal for the Wild from 2000 to 2007, his uncle Jacques Lemaire was the team's head coach. Fernandez was acquired with Brad Lukowich in a trade for draft picks with Dallas in June 2000. He played 260 regular-season contests with Minnesota and posted a record of 113-102-28 with a .914 save percentage and a 2.47 goals-against average.

6. In June 2000, the Wild selected goaltender Mike Vernon from Florida in the NHL expansion draft. Vernon was a former All-Star who had won two Stanley Cups as well as a William M. Jennings Trophy and the Conn Smythe Trophy. Minnesota then traded him to Calgary the same day for the rights to Dan Cavanaugh and an eighth-round draft pick. Vernon never played another NHL game, though, and retired two years later at the age of 39.

7. As of 2020, Nicklas Bäckström was the Wild's all-time leading netminder in games played and he held several other club records including wins, losses, and shutouts. He signed as an undrafted free agent in 2006 and posted a 194-142-50 record in 409 outings with the Wild, with a 2.48 goals-against average and a .915 save percentage. In 2006-07, Bäckström shared the William M. Jennings Trophy with teammate Manny Fernandez and led the league in goals-against average (1.97) and save percentage (.929).

8. Zac Bierk played just one game in goal with the Wild and it came in their inaugural season, when Manny Fernandez and Jamie McLennan were both injured. He faced New Jersey on March 8, 2001, and lost the game 6-2. Bierk is probably best known as being the younger brother of Sebastian Bach, the ex-lead singer of rock band Skid Row, and the brother of Canadian actress Dylan Bierk. Four other brothers and his late father are also well-known artists.

9. After leaving Minnesota to sign with Phoenix as a free agent in 2001, Zac Bierk made NHL history on January 8, 2003, in a game against Chicago. The contest finished in a 0-0 tie as Bierk and Blackhawks' goalie Michael Leighton both recorded their first NHL shutouts. It was the first time in league history that both goaltenders posted their first career shutouts in the same game.

10. The Wild selected Jamie "Noodles" McLennan in the 2000 NHL expansion draft from St. Louis after he had won the Bill Masterton Trophy in 1997-98. McLennan didn't have much luck with the Wild, even though he played well. He posted a .905 save percentage and 2.64 goals average in 38 games in 2000-01 with a 5-23-9 record. As luck would have it, he wasn't credited with a win when he posted his first shutout of the campaign as it came in a 0-0 tie with Florida. McLennan didn't play with the club in 2001-02 and was traded to Calgary in June 2002.

CHAPTER 10:

ODDS AND ENDS

QUIZ TIME!

1. For how many seasons did the Wild play in the Northwest Division?

    a. 10
    b. 11
    c. 12
    d. 13

2. Minnesota tied how many regular-season games through the club's first four seasons?

    a. 47
    b. 38
    c. 55
    d. 61

3. Minnesota's mascot is named Nordy.

    a. True
    b. False

4. Who scored the first hat trick for the Wild, on November 26, 2000?

   a. Wes Walz
   b. Marián Gáborík
   c. Scott Pellerin
   d. Antti Laaksonen

5. What was the first penalty ever called on the Wild?

   a. High sticking
   b. Charging
   c. Tripping
   d. Interference

6. Who was given the team's first penalty?

   a. Ladislav Benýšek
   b. Matt Johnson
   c. Curtis Leschyshyn
   d. Sergei Krivokrasov

7. In what year did the Wild host the All-Star Game for the first time?

   a. 2008
   b. 2002
   c. 2004
   d. 2007

8. Nobody scored on a penalty shot attempt in the club's first season.

   a. True
   b. False

9. Before dedicating his life to hockey, which former Wild player was going to college to become a plumber?

    a. Filip Kuba

    b. Tyler Ennis

    c. Nino Niederreiter

    d. Marián Gáborík

10. In the 2017-18 season, Devan Dubnyk set which team record for goalies?

    a. Most losses

    b. Most penalty minutes

    c. Most shootout wins

    d. Most starts

11. The Minnesota Wild has three minor-league affiliate teams as of 2020.

    a. True

    b. False

12. How many times has the Wild made the playoffs as of 2019?

    a. 6

    b. 7

    c. 8

    d. 9

13. In 2010-11, the Wild won how many faceoffs?

    a. 2,408

    b. 2,336

    c. 2,371

    d. 2,385

14. The Wild lost their first NHL game on home ice.

    a. True
    b. False

15. As of the 2018-19 season, what is the Wild's official goal song?

    a. Born to Be Wild, by Steppenwolf
    b. Rock and Roll Part 2, by Gary Glitter
    c. Let's Go Crazy, by Prince
    d. *Crowd Chant*, by Joe Satriani

16. Who scored the team's only hat trick in 2018-19?

    a. Jason Zucker
    b. Mikko Koivu
    c. Eric Staal
    d. Jared Spurgeon

17. How many players had a negative plus/minus rating in 2009-10?

    a. 16
    b. 14
    c. 26
    d. 35

18. As of 2019, what is the most wins the Wild has posted in a regular season?

    a. 51
    b. 47
    c. 50
    d. 49

19. Who scored the Wild's first penalty shot goal?

    a. Sébastien Bordeleau

    b. Stacy Roest

    c. Andrew Brunette

    d. Pascal Dupuis

20. Only one player appeared in all 82 games in the Wild's inaugural season.

    a. True

    b. False

QUIZ ANSWERS

1. C – 12

2. C – 55

3. A – True

4. D – Antti Laaksonen

5. B – Charging

6. B – Matt Johnson

7. C – 2004

8. A – True

9. C – Nino Niederreiter

10. B – Most penalty minutes

11. B – False

12. D – 9

13. A – 2408

14. B – False

15. D – *Crowd Chant*, by Joe Satriani

16. A – Jason Zucker

17. C – 26

18. D – 49

19. A – Sébastien Bordeleau

20. B – False

DID YOU KNOW?

1. The Wild has had six head coaches since the team's inception. Jacques Lemaire was first and remained until the end of 2008-09. Todd Richards took after Lemaire left and was fired in April 2011. Mike Yeo was hired in June 2011 and sacked in February 2016, when John Torchetti was named the team's interim head coach. Bruce Boudreau took over in May 2016 and was let go on February 14, 2020. Assistant coach Dean Evason was named interim coach and then hired as head coach on July 13, 2020.

2. Jacques Lemaire coached the most regular-season games (656) and posted the most wins (293), most losses (255), most ties/overtime/shootout defeats (108), and the most points (694). He also coached the most playoff games (29), shares the record for most wins with Mike Yeo (11), and lost the most games (18). Lemaire is the only Wild coach to win the Jack Adams Award, which he received for the 2002-03 season.

3. The only head coaching category in which Jacques Lemaire doesn't lead the organization is winning percentage. Bruce Boudreau's regular-season winning percentage of .579 leads the club and Lemaire's mark of .529 ranks fourth. Mike Yeo owns the top winning percentage in the playoffs at .393, while Lemaire ranks second at .379.

4. The club has had four general managers from its entry into the NHL to 2020. Doug Risebrough held the job from

September 2, 1999, to April 16, 2009; Chuck Fletcher held the post from May 22, 2009, to April 23, 2018; Paul Fenton took over from May 21, 2018, to July 30, 2019, and Bill Guerin was hired on August 21, 2019.

5. Doug Risebrough led the club to one division title and three playoff appearances as general manager while Chuck Fletcher's teams made the postseason on six occasions. Paul Fenton failed to make the playoffs in his tenure while Bill Guerin's squad reached the adjusted play-in system in 2019-20 when the league was affected by the Covid-19 pandemic.

6. In 2002-03, the Wild became the first team in NHL playoff history to win two playoff series in a season after trailing 3-1 in games. They stormed back to beat the Colorado Avalanche in seven games in the first round and repeated the comeback in the second round against the Vancouver Canucks. The Wild won Games 6 and 7 against Colorado in overtime.

7. When the 2003-04 season faced off, both Marián Gáborík and Pascal Dupuis sat out due to contract disputes. After new deals were eventually signed, Dupuis played 59 of 82 games with 11 goals and 26 points while Gáborík appeared in 65 games while posting 18 goals and 40 points. The Wild struggled that season without the two wingers and failed to make the playoffs with a record of 30-29-20-3.

8. During the 2004-05 NHL lockout, former Wild forward Sergei Zholtok returned to Europe to play. Sadly, while

skating for Riga 2000 against Dinamo Minsk on Nov. 3, 2004, he left the contest with five minutes remaining due to cardiac arrhythmia. He collapsed in the dressing room and passed away in the arms of Riga teammate Darby Hendrickson, who was also Zholtok's teammate with the Wild. Zholtok was just 31 years old.

9. In the summer of 2012, the Wild signed unrestricted free agent defenseman Ryan Suter and winger Zach Parise to identical contracts that paid the players US$98 million over 13 years. Both players were still with the club in 2019-20. Parise's father, Jean-Paul Parise, played with the Minnesota North Stars NHL franchise when he was younger and Zach was born in Minneapolis.

10. The NHL realigned the league from six to four divisions in 2013 and the Northwest Division, which the Wild played in, was eliminated. The franchise then joined the Central Division with the Winnipeg Jets, Colorado Avalanche, Chicago Blackhawks, Dallas Stars, Nashville Predators, and St. Louis Blues.

CHAPTER 11:

BLUES ON THE BLUE LINE

QUIZ TIME!

1. Which defenseman scored 34 points in the Wild's first season?

    a. Filip Kuba

    b. Ľubomír Sekeráš

    c. Sean O'Donnell

    d. Brad Bombardir

2. Who had the highest plus/minus rating in 2006-07?

    a. Brent Burns

    b. Martin Skoula

    c. Shawn Belle

    d. Keith Carney

3. Matt Dumba was the only defender to register over 100 hits and 100 blocked shots in 2017-18.

    a. True

    b. False

4. How many rearguards played at least one game for the Wild in the 2005-06 season?

    a. 10
    b. 9
    c. 11
    d. 12

5. Who doled out 128 hits in 2014-15?

    a. Nate Prosser
    b. Jared Spurgeon
    c. Jonas Brodin
    d. Ryan Suter

6. What was Greg Pateryn's plus/minus rating in 2018-19?

    a. -8
    b. +11
    c. +14
    d. -11

7. This blue-liner was the only Wild player to skate in all 82 games in 2007-08.

    a. Brent Burns
    b. Nick Schultz
    c. Martin Skoula
    d. Kim Johnsson

8. Ryan Suter was the first Wild defenseman to score a hat trick.

    a. True
    b. False

9. Who scored the only short-handed goal for Minnesota in the 2013-14 playoffs?

    a. Jared Spurgeon

    b. Marco Scandella

    c. Keith Ballard

    d. Nate Prosser

10. How many defensemen played at least one game in the 2010-11 season?

    a. 10

    b. 14

    c. 12

    d. 15

11. Nick Seeler led the Wild with 64 penalty minutes in 2018-19.

    a. True

    b. False

12. Which defender tallied 10 power-play goals in 2008-09?

    a. Kurtis Foster

    b. Kim Johnsson

    c. Marc-Andre Bergeron

    d. Marek Zidlicky

13. How many defensemen had over 100 hits in 2015-16?

    a. 2

    b. 3

    c. 4

    d. 5

14. Clayton Stoner led the Wild with 117 penalty minutes in 2012-13.

    a. True
    b. False

15. How many points did Brent Burns register in 2010-11?

    a. 60
    b. 48
    c. 37
    d. 46

16. Which defenseman scored 2 game-winning goals in 2007-08?

    a. Sean Hill
    b. Kurtis Foster
    c. Petteri Nummelin
    d. Nick Schultz

17. Who had 148 penalty minutes in 2001-02?

    a. Jason Marshall
    b. Willie Mitchell
    c. Brad Brown
    d. Ladislav Benýšek

18. How many assists did Ryan Suter earn in 2014-15?

    a. 31
    b. 22
    c. 49
    d. 36

19. Which defenseman notched 21 points in 2003-04?

    a. Darby Hendrickson

    b. Willie Mitchell

    c. Filip Kuba

    d. Andrei Zyuzin

20. Three defensemen played all 82 games for Minnesota in the 2008-09 season.

    a. True

    b. False

QUIZ ANSWERS

1. B – Ľubomír Sekeráš

2. D – Keith Carney

3. A – True

4. C – 10

5. C – Jonas Brodin

6. D – -11

7. A – Brent Burns

8. A – True

9. B – Marco Scandella

10. C – 12

11. A – True

12. D – Marek Zidlicky

13. C – 4

14. B – False

15. D – 46

16. B – Kurtis Foster

17. A – Jason Marshall

18. D – 36

19. D – Andrei Zyuzin

20. B – False

DID YOU KNOW?

1. The highest-scoring defender in Wild history is Ryan Suter, who had tallied 52 goals and 350 points in 600 games by the end of the 2019-20 regular season, with a +53 rating. Suter holds the mark for most points in a season by a Wild blue-liner with 51 in 2015-16. He also holds team highs for best plus/minus in a season (+34), which he shares with Jason Zucker, and most ice time per game in a season (29:25).

2. Jared Spurgeon has also been a consistent contributor from the blue line after being drafted 156th overall by the New York Islanders in 2008. He never played a game for the Islanders, though, as he signed as a free agent with the Wild in September 2010. Since then he's posted 82 goals and 280 points in 653 outings, as of the conclusion of the 2019-20 regular season. Spurgeon is also reliable in his own end, as shown by his +50 rating.

3. The Wild isn't known for their physical play and the most-penalized rearguard in club annals is Willie Mitchell. He was assessed 333 minutes for the team in 288 regular-season games from 2000-01 to 2005-06. Mitchell went on to log 787 penalty minutes in 907 career NHL games, with another 90 minutes in 89 playoff encounters.

4. As of 2019, Matt Dumba has been the highest-drafted defenseman by the Wild. Dumba was taken seventh

overall in the 2012 draft and made his NHL debut at the age of 19. Dumba had played in 411 regular-season games by the end of the 2019-20 regular season and had just turned 26 years of age. He's chipped in with 62 goals, 174 points, and a +27 rating.

5. One of the calmest and most poised Wild blue-liners is Jonas Brodin, who was drafted 11th overall by the club in 2011. At the end of the 2019-20 regular season, he had tallied 30 goals and 146 points in 555 outings, with a +47 rating. The Wild were so impressed with his play in the early going that they signed him to a six-year contract extension worth $25 million in October 2014.

6. The Wild drafted Nick Leddy 16th overall in 2009 but didn't give him a chance to prove himself. His rights were traded to Chicago with Kim Johnsson eight months later for fellow defender Cam Barker. Leddy helped the Blackhawks win the 2013 Stanley Cup and was later traded to the New York Islanders. At the end of the 2019-20 regular season, he had notched 305 points in 720 regular-season NHL contests. Barker was placed on waivers by the Wild in June 2011 to buy out his contract.

7. One former first-round draft pick that didn't work out for Minnesota was Tyler Cuma. The blue-liner was chosen 23rd overall in 2008 but played just one NHL game in the 2011-12 regular season. He spent most of his time with the Wild's AHL affiliate, where he posted 2 goals and 33 points in 201 regular-season outings. Cuma then left the club in 2014 to play in Europe.

8. Anthony James (A.J.) Thelen was similar to Tyler Cuma in that he was also a first-round draft selection who didn't crack the Wild's lineup. Thelen was taken 12th overall by the team in 2004 from Michigan State University. He never signed with Minnesota, though, and played in the East Coast Hockey League. Thelen suffered from concussions and back problems and retired from the game in 2011 at the age of 25. He posted an impressive 102 points in 210 ECHL games.

9. In January 2020, Wild blue-liner Greg Pateryn dressed for the night's game against Pittsburgh as he usually did. However, on-ice officials then visited the team's bench before the opening faceoff to remove him from the game. This was due to head coach Bruce Boudreau forgetting to add his name to the lineup card. The Wild were left with five defenders and were blown out 7-3. Boudreau admitted to the mistake and took full responsibility.

10. Minnesota selected defender Curtis Leschyshyn from Carolina in the 2000 NHL entry draft. He wouldn't complete the team's NHL debut season though, as he was traded to Ottawa in March 2001. Leschyshyn played for two NHL teams which relocated: He was with the Quebec Nordiques when they moved to Colorado and the Hartford Whalers when they moved to Carolina. He won a Stanley Cup with Colorado and played 1,033 regular-season NHL games from 1988 to 2004.

CHAPTER 12:

CENTERS OF ATTENTION

QUIZ TIME!

1. Which center played all 82 games in the Wild's inaugural season?

    a. Wes Walz

    b. Aaron Gavey

    c. Jim Dowd

    d. Pavel Patera

2. How many goals did Eric Staal score in 2017-18?

    a. 40

    b. 27

    c. 42

    d. 38

3. Sergei Zholtok scored 15 power-play goals in 2001-02.

    a. True

    b. False

4. Who was the only Minnesota center with over 100 hits in 2018-19?

a. Joel Eriksson Ek

b. Luke Kunin

c. Eric Staal

d. Charlie Coyle

5. This center posted 169 points in 446 regular-season contests with the Wild.

a. Ryan Carter

b. Kyle Brodziak

c. Marc Chouinard

d. Matt Cullen

6. How many faceoffs did Mikko Koivu win in 2014-15?

a. 746

b. 924

c. 988

d. 989

7. This center posted 79 points in 2005-06.

a. Randy Robitaille

b. Pierre-Marc Bouchard

c. Todd White

d. Brian Rolston

8. Daniel Winnik tallied 29 points in his only season with the Wild.

a. True

b. False

9. Which center had the fewest penalty minutes in 2006-07?

    a. Wes Walz

    b. Todd White

    c. Pierre-Marc Bouchard

    d. Wyatt Smith

10. Who contributed 24 assists in 2007-08?

    a. Eric Belanger

    b. Dominic Moore

    c. James Sheppard

    d. Steve Kelly

11. Four centers played 80 games in the 2016-17 season.

    a. True

    b. False

12. What was Kyle Brodziak's plus/minus rating in 2014-15?

    a. +13

    b. -6

    c. +9

    d. -3

13. Who was the only center to play all 82 games in 2008-09?

    a. Dan Fritsche

    b. Colton Gilles

    c. Krys Kolanos

    d. James Sheppard

14. Zenon Konopka had 117 penalty minutes in only 37 games in 2012-13.

a. True

b. False

15. How many game-winning goals did Wild centers score in 2009-10?

    a. 5

    b. 8

    c. 10

    d. 13

16. What was Mikko Koivu's faceoff win percentage in 2015-16?

    a. 56.7

    b. 55.3

    c. 56.2

    d. 53.3

17. Who scored 69 points in 2016-17?

    a. Eric Staal

    b. Mikael Granlund

    c. Mikko Koivu

    d. Charlie Coyle

18. How many shots on goal did Brian Rolston take in 2005-06?

    a. 127

    b. 151

    c. 252

    d. 293

19. Which center scored 35 points in 2011-12?

   a. Cody Almond
   b. Erik Christenson
   c. Darroll Powe
   d. Matt Cullen

20. In 2009-10, Andrew Ebbett was the only center to score at least 10 goals and 10 assists for Minnesota.

   a. True
   b. False

QUIZ ANSWERS

1. A – Wes Walz

2. C – 42

3. B – False

4. A – Joel Eriksson Ek

5. B – Kyle Brodziak

6. D – 989

7. D – Brian Rolston

8. B – False

9. C – Pierre-Marc Bouchard

10. A – Eric Belanger

11. A – True

12. B – -6

13. D – James Sheppard

14. A – True

15. C – 10

16. C – 56.2

17. B – Mikael Granlund

18. D – 293

19. D – Matt Cullen

20. B – False

DID YOU KNOW?

1. The top center in Wild history has certainly been Mikko Koivu, the club's all-team leading scorer and most recent captain. He was drafted sixth overall by the team in 2001 and has played his entire career with the franchise. When the 2019-20 campaign concluded, he had amassed 205 goals and 504 assists for 709 points, with a +70 rating. Koivu had also chipped in with 28 points in 55 playoff contests.

2. Wes Walz was a popular center with the team after signing as a free agent in June 2000. He played until he was 37 years old and retired following the 2007-08 season. He skated in 438 regular-season games and recorded 182 points and 272 penalty minutes. Walz was also a fine penalty killer who notched a club-record 14 shorthanded goals, with half of those coming in one season.

3. The Wild drafted Mikael Granlund ninth overall in 2010 and he played just over six seasons with the squad. Granlund was a steady contributor with 93 goals, 317 points, and a +32 rating in 461 outings. He added 21 points in 39 postseason matches. Granlund was traded to Nashville in February 2019 for winger Kevin Fiala.

4. Center Marc Chouinard played with Minnesota alongside his cousin Eric Chouinard in 2004. Eric played just 31 games with the team in 2003-04 after being acquired in a trade from Philadelphia. He posted 7 points and left the

club in October 2004. Marc signed as a free agent in July 2003 and notched 51 points in 119 games before leaving to sign with Vancouver in 2006.

5. Dominic Moore was a fine depth player over the course of his NHL career with 282 points in 897 regular-season games. He played with 10 different teams between 2004 and 2018 and won the Bill Masterton Trophy for 2013-14 but struggled in Minnesota. Moore was acquired from Pittsburgh in a February 2007 trade and notched just 5 points in 40 games before being placed on waivers 11 months later.

6. There have been four NHL-playing Staal brothers, Eric, Jordan, Jared, and Marc. Eric signed with the Wild as a free agent in 2016, when he was a 32-year-old veteran. He tallied 28 goals and 65 points in his first season and improved to 42 goals and 76 points the next campaign. The 42 goals tied Marián Gáborík for the most in a season by a Wild player. Staal has scored 240 points in 311 regular-season games with Minnesota by the end of 2019-20, with 1,021 points in 1,240 career games.

7. After being drafted first overall by Ottawa in 1993, center Alexandre Daigle was considered by many to be one of the biggest draft busts in history. However, he played well for the Wild during the last two seasons of his NHL career. Daigle signed as a free agent in September 2003 and tallied 79 points in 124 regular-season games. He left to play in Europe in 2005 after posting 327 points in 616 NHL contests with six different teams.

8. Landon Ferraro made the most of his limited ice time when called up by the Wild for two games in 2017-18. He scored a goal on three shots for a 33.3 shooting percentage while playing just an average of 4:25 per game. The center signed as a free agent in 2017 and left for Germany two years later after failing to receive another call-up to Minnesota. His father, Ray Ferraro, tallied 898 points in 1,258 regular-season NHL games.

9. One of the longest-serving Wild players has been Pierre-Marc Bouchard, who played 565 regular-season games with the team and 21 in the playoffs. He was drafted eighth overall by the club in 2002 and racked up 347 points, adding nine in the postseason. Bouchard, who was a cousin of former NHL player P.A. Parenteau, signed as a free agent with the New York Islanders in 2013. He once missed 13 months of action and 112 games with Minnesota due to post-concussion syndrome. He retired in 2016 at the age of 31.

10. Many Wild fans may know assistant coach Darby Hendrickson from his days as a color commentator on the team's television broadcasts. However, he also played for the team after being chosen in the 2000 NHL expansion draft from Vancouver. Hendrickson registered 60 points in 182 games with the club and added t points in their 18-game playoff run of 2002-03. He was also one of the Wild's numerous captains in their inaugural season.

CHAPTER 13:

THE WINGERS TAKE FLIGHT

QUIZ TIME!

1. Who scored 25 goals in 2015-16?

   a. Zach Parise

   b. Nino Niederreiter

   c. Thomas Vanek

   d. Jason Pominville

2. How many assists did Pascal Dupuis contribute in 2005-06?

   a. 12

   b. 18

   c. 16

   d. 20

3. Scott Pellerin had a +8 rating in the team's first season.

   a. True

   b. False

4. Who scored 14 power-play goals in 2009-10?

    a. Guillaume Latendresse
    b. Andrew Brunette
    c. Antti Miettinen
    d. Martin Havlat

5. How many assists did Marián Gáborík tally in 2001-02?

    a. 20
    b. 30
    c. 48
    d. 37

6. What was Dany Heatley's team-low plus/minus rating in 2013-14?

    a. -18
    b. +7
    c. -11
    d. +14

7. Who led the Wild in penalty minutes with 177 in 2003-04?

    a. Antti Laaksonen
    b. Richard Park
    c. Matt Johnson
    d. Alex Henry

8. Jason Zucker scored 7 game-winning goals in 2018-19.

    a. True
    b. False

9. How many wingers played at least 80 games in the 2002-03 campaign?

    a. 4
    b. 5
    c. 6
    d. 7

10. This winger had 21 points and 94 penalty minutes in 2016-17.

    a. Jason Pominville
    b. Chris Stewart
    c. Teemu Pulkkinen
    d. Jason Zucker

11. Stéphane Veilleux had a minus-27 rating in 2008-09.

    a. True
    b. False

12. Which winger had 155 hits in 2012-13?

    a. Torrey Mitchell
    b. Dany Heatley
    c. Devin Setoguchi
    d. Cal Clutterbuck

13. How many points did Minnesota wingers combine for in the 2006-07 playoffs?

    a. 7
    b. 10
    c. 12
    d. 15

14. Zach Parise led the Wild in the 2013-14 postseason with 14 points.

   a. True
   b. False

15. How many points did Richard Park notch in his three seasons with Minnesota?

   a. 38
   b. 44
   c. 67
   d. 74

16. This winger scored 8 game-winning goals in 2002-03.

   a. Jeremy Stevenson
   b. Marián Gáborík
   c. Antti Laaksonen
   d. Pascal Dupuis

17. Who took 146 shots on net in 2011-12?

   a. Warren Peters
   b. Nick Johnson
   c. Jed Ortmeyer
   d. Brad Staubitz

18. Which winger scored 54 points in the first 69 games of the 2019-20 season?

   a. Kevin Fiala
   b. Zach Parise
   c. Mats Zuccarello
   d. Jordan Greenway

19. How many points did Andrew Brunette register in the 2002-03 playoffs?

    a. 9

    b. 10

    c. 13

    d. 17

20. Devin Setoguchi was the only winger to play all 48 games for the Wild in 2012-13.

    a. True

    b. False

QUIZ ANSWERS

1. A – Zach Parise

2. C – 16

3. B – False

4. B – Andrew Brunette

5. D – 37

6. A – -18

7. C – Matt Johnson

8. A – True

9. C – 6

10. B – Chris Stewart

11. B – False

12. D – Cal Clutterbuck

13. C – 12

14. A – True

15. D – 74

16. B – Marián Gáborík

17. B – Nick Johnson

18. A – Kevin Fiala

19. C – 13

20. A – True

DID YOU KNOW?

1. There was a lot of pressure on Devin Setoguchi when he arrived in Minnesota with Charlie Coyle from San Jose in a 2011 trade. The main reason was that he was drafted eighth overall by the Sharks in 2005 and the Wild gave up future star Brent Burns to get him. Setoguchi notched 63 points in 117 regular-season games before being traded to Winnipeg for a fourth-round draft pick in July 2013.

2. When it comes to the Wild's power play, winger Zach Parise has proven to be the team's specialist. At the conclusion of the 2019-20 regular season, he was the team's all-time leader with 69 power-play goals. In addition, 116 of the 382 points he had posted with the team had come with the man advantage.

3. One of the NHL's most underrated players was Andrew Brunette. He signed with Minnesota as a free agent in July 2001, stayed for four years, and returned as a free agent in 2008 for three more years. Brunette notched 321 points in 489 games with the Wild and added 13 points in their 2002-03 playoff run. He owns the club's record for shooting percentage at 18.1 and led the league in 2009-10. Brunette posted 733 points in 1,110 career NHL outings, along with 35 points in 49 postseason matches.

4. Jason Zucker was a fixture on the wing for Minnesota from 2011-12 to February 10, 2020, when he was traded to

Pittsburgh for Alexander Galchenyuk, Calen Addison, and a conditional first-round draft pick. Zucker contributed 132 goals and 243 points in 456 regular-season games and led the league with a +34 rating in 2016-17. The +34 ties defender Ryan Suter for the Wild's franchise record in a season.

5. Minnesota acquired Jason Pominville from Buffalo in an April 2013 trade and then swapped him back to the Sabres just over four years later. In the meantime, he played 327 outings with the club and chipped in with 206 points and a +24 rating. He also added 23 points in 36 postseason tilts. Pominville led Minnesota in scoring in 2013-14 with 30 goals and 30 assists.

6. After being traded to Dallas from the New York Rangers in February 2019, Mats Zuccarello decided he'd rather play in Minnesota. The 32-year-old native of Oslo, Norway, signed as a free agent on July 1 and scored 15 goals and 37 points in his first regular-season campaign with the team in 2019-20. Zuccarello's contract with the Wild is for five years and a total of $30 million.

7. Another relative newcomer to the Wild is winger Kevin Fiala, who was acquired at the 2018-19 trade deadline from Nashville for Mikael Granlund. He signed a two-year extension with the team seven months later. Fiala posted just 3 goals and 7 points in 19 games after arriving. However, he picked things up with 23 goals and a team-leading 54 points in 64 games in 2019-20, with 9 power play-markers and 4 game-winners.

8. Although he was undrafted, Pascal Dupuis managed to play in the NHL from 2000-01 to 2015-16 in a career that started in Minnesota. He signed as a free agent in 2000, just before the puck dropped on the team's first NHL season. Dupuis tallied 141 points in 334 outings, with 8 points in 16 playoff clashes before being traded to the New York Rangers in February 2007. He went on to win a Stanley Cup with Pittsburgh in 2009 and led the NHL in plus/minus rating in 2012-13. Dupuis was forced to retire in 2015 due to blood clots.

9. One of the NHL's best-known enforcers started his NHL career with the Wild. After going undrafted, John Scott signed as a free agent in December 2006. The 6-foot-8-inch winger scored 1 goal and 3 points in 71 games over two seasons with 111 minutes in penalties. Scott ended his career with 5 goals, 11 points, and 544 penalty minutes in 286 regular-season games over 8 years. He famously played in the 2016 NHL All-Star Game, in which he was captain of the Pacific Division and was named the game's MVP. Scott also appeared in the television series S.W.A.T. In 2017.

10. Since nine members of the famous Sutter clan have played in the NHL, so far it's not surprising that at least one of them has suited up for the Wild. Brett Sutter signed as a free agent in July 2014 and played in 6 games that season while earning 3 assists and 4 penalty minutes, playing an average of 9:19 minutes per outing. Sutter was then traded in February 2016 to Los Angeles for Scott Sabourin.

CHAPTER 14:

THE HEATED RIVALRIES

QUIZ TIME!

1. Which club has the Wild beaten 55 times in 94 regular-season matchups?

    a. Chicago Blackhawks

    b. Edmonton Oilers

    c. Vancouver Canucks

    d. Calgary Flames

2. How many teams did the Wild lose three or more games to in the 2013-14 season?

    a. 3

    b. 1

    c. 4

    d. 2

3. The Colorado Avalanche was the first team the Wild faced over 100 times in regular-season play.

    a. True

    b. False

4. Against which team did the Wild clinch 5 points in 4 games during the 2012-13 season?

   a. Los Angeles Kings
   b. Detroit Red Wings
   c. Columbus Blue Jackets
   d. Nashville Predators

5. This team scored 23 goals against the Wild in 2005-06.

   a. Vancouver Canucks
   b. Phoenix Coyotes
   c. Dallas Stars
   d. Calgary Flames

6. Which team has the Wild scored 88 goals against through 27 regular-season games?

   a. New York Islanders
   b. Tampa Bay Lightning
   c. New York Rangers
   d. Florida Panthers

7. Which club eliminated the Wild in their first playoff appearance?

   a. Colorado Avalanche
   b. St. Louis Blues
   c. Mighty Ducks of Anaheim
   d. Edmonton Oilers

8. Minnesota has given up 252 goals to the Dallas Stars in 79 regular-season contests.

   a. True
   b. False

9. Which of these teams did the Wild not win a game against in 2016-17?

    a. Boston Bruins

    b. Washington Capitals

    c. Carolina Hurricanes

    d. Pittsburgh Penguins

10. How many teams did Minnesota record 10 points against in 2007-08?

    a. 1

    b. 4

    c. 2

    d. 3

11. Minnesota won six of its first eight regular-season games against the Vegas Golden Knights.

    a. True

    b. False

12. How many goals did the Wild score against Edmonton in the 2005-06 season?

    a. 18

    b. 22

    c. 27

    d. 30

13. The Wild blew away the New York Islanders by what score on March 18, 2014?

    a. 8-2

    b. 6-0

c. 7-0

d. 9-1

14. The Wild was eliminated in three straight postseasons by Chicago from 2013 to 2015.

    a. True

    b. False

15. Against how many teams did the Wild score 10 or more goals in 2007-08?

    a. 6

    b. 7

    c. 8

    d. 9

16. How many teams beat the Wild in overtime in the 2015-16 regular season?

    a. 6

    b. 5

    c. 8

    d. 10

17. Against which team did the Wild play two regular-season games in Finland in 2010-11?

    a. Boston Bruins

    b. San Jose Sharks

    c. Columbus Blue Jackets

    d. Carolina Hurricanes

18. Which team has the Wild lost nine overtime games to through 61 regular-season meetings?

a. Detroit Red Wings

b. St. Louis Blues

c. New Jersey Devils

d. Winnipeg Jets

19. Which team did Minnesota lose all five games to in regulation time in their first season?

a. Colorado Avalanche

b. Mighty Ducks of Anaheim

c. San Jose Sharks

d. Phoenix Coyotes

20. The Wild has a 3-12 playoff game record against the St. Louis Blues as of 2019.

a. True

b. False

QUIZ ANSWERS

1. B – Edmonton Oilers

2. D – 2

3. A – True

4. C – Columbus Blue Jackets

5. D – Calgary Flames

6. D – Florida Panthers

7. C – Mighty Ducks of Anaheim

8. B – False

9. B – Washington Capitals

10. D – 3

11. A – True

12. C – 27

13. B – 6-0

14. A – True

15. D – 9

16. C – 8

17. D – Carolina Hurricanes

18. A – Detroit Red Wings

19. A – Colorado Avalanche

20. B – False

DID YOU KNOW?

1. The Wild entered the NHL in 2000-01 along with the Columbus Blue Jackets so a natural rivalry was born with Columbus, even though the teams play in different conferences. The teams had met 60 times by the end of the 2019-20 regular season with Minnesota having a 29-30-1 won-lost-tied record. The teams have never met in the playoffs.

2. There is also a natural rivalry with the Dallas Stars since that franchise was based in Minnesota until 1993. The squads have met just once in the postseason, with Dallas winning the first-round series in six games in 2015-16. The teams now play in the same division. Minnesota's all-time regular and postseason record against Dallas at the end of the 2019-20 regular season was 35-49-1.

3. Minnesota's closest geographical rivals are Winnipeg and Chicago. The Wild's all-time regular and postseason record against the Jets at the end of the 2019-20 regular season was 25-23-1 and their record against the Blackhawks was 46-45-1.

4. The Wild vs Blackhawks rivalry heated up in the 2012-13 playoffs, when they met in the first round, which Chicago won in five games. The Central Division rivals met again in the 2013-14 postseason and Chicago won the second-round series in six games. It was *deja vu* in 2014-15, when

they battled yet again in the second round; this time, Chicago swept the Wild in four outings. The clubs also met in the 2016 NHL Stadium Series in Minneapolis, with the Wild winning 6-1.

5. The Wild's playoff record as of 2019-20 was 26-47 after a total of 73 games. They have played seven different teams in the postseason for a total of 13 series. The club's record in those series is 4-9. They have winning series records against Vancouver (1-0) and Colorado (2-1), with an even mark against St. Louis (1-1) and losing records against Chicago (0-3), Anaheim (0-2), Dallas (0-1), and Winnipeg (0-1)

6. The team the Wild has had the most success against, based on winning percentage, is the Vegas Golden Knights. Minnesota held a 6-2 record by the end of the 2019-20 regular season for a 75 percent winning mark. The team the Wild has the most trouble with historically is the New Jersey Devils with a record of 8-15-2 for a 36 percent winning percentage.

7. The Wild has fared relatively well against the "Original Six" NHL franchises with the following overall regular and postseason records against these teams: Montreal (15-9-1), Boston (14-12-0), Chicago (46-45-1), Toronto (12-12-0), New York Rangers (12-16-0), and Detroit (21-37-3).

8. Minnesota fans quickly came to dislike the Anaheim Ducks, as the Ducks ended the Wild's first two playoff runs. The Wild made the postseason for the first time in

2002-03 with Anaheim sweeping them in four games in the Western Conference Final. Minnesota made the playoffs again in 2006-07 and the Ducks bounced them in five games in the first round.

9. The only team to play in the same division as the Wild since Minnesota entered the NHL has been the Colorado Avalanche. They met in the 2002-03 playoffs, when Colorado held a 3-1 lead in games only to see the Wild storm back and take the first-round series. The clubs met again in 2007-08, with Colorado exacting revenge in six games. Their last meeting came in 2013-14, when the Wild won Game 7 in dramatic fashion in overtime. The Wild has met Colorado more than any other team and had an all-time regular and postseason mark of 63-60-3 at the end of the 2019-20 regular season.

10. Each NHL team has a least-favorite city to visit; Minnesota's graveyards are Washington and Carolina. The Wild's winning percentage in both of those towns is just 25 percent with identical 3-9 records as of the end of the 2019-20 regular-season campaign.

CHAPTER 15:

THE AWARDS SECTION

QUIZ TIME!

1. Who was the first Wild player to appear in an NHL All-Star Game?

   a. Dwayne Roloson
   b. Filip Kuba
   c. Marián Gáborík
   d. Manny Fernandez

2. What was the first major NHL award won by a member of the Wild?

   a. Ted Lindsay Award
   b. William M. Jennings Award
   c. Roger Crozier Saving Grace Award
   d. Jack Adams Award

3. As of 2019-20, Minnesota has finished first in its division twice.

   a. True
   b. False

4. Who was the first Wild player selected to the NHL All-Rookie team?

    a. Charlie Coyle

    b. Jason Zucker

    c. Jonas Brodin

    d. Jared Spurgeon

5. Which player was not selected for two or more All-Star Games?

    a. Nicklas Bäckström

    b. Devan Dubnyk

    c. Eric Staal

    d. Ryan Suter

6. Who was the Wild's first recipient of the Jack Adams Award?

    a. Bruce Boudreau

    b. Jacques Lemaire

    c. Mike Yeo

    d. Todd Richards

7. Which forward won the King Clancy Memorial Trophy in 2018-19?

    a. Zach Parise

    b. Mikael Granlund

    c. Mikko Koivu

    d. Jason Zucker

8. As of 2020, no former member of the Wild has been inducted into the Hockey Hall of Fame.

a. True

b. False

9. Which goalie was the first to win the Roger Crozier Saving Grace Award for Minnesota?

    a. Josh Harding

    b. Nicklas Bäckström

    c. Dwayne Roloson

    d. Manny Fernandez

10. Who finished 3rd in voting for the Frank J. Selke Award in 2016-17?

    a. Mikael Granlund

    b. Eric Fehr

    c. Mikko Koivu

    d. Marcus Foligno

11. Devan Dubnyk finished 5th in voting for the Vezina Trophy in 2016-17.

    a. True

    b. False

12. What award did goaltender Josh Harding win in 2012-13?

    a. Vezina Trophy

    b. William M. Jennings Award

    c. Ted Lindsay Award

    d. Bill Masterton Memorial Trophy

13. How many goals did Nicklas Bäckström and Manny Fernandez allow when they shared the William M. Jennings Trophy in 2006-07?

a. 183

b. 176

c. 165

d. 173

14. Nicklas Bäckström was the last NHL goalie to win the Roger Crozier Saving Grace Award in 2006-07.

    a. True

    b. False

15. Where did Marián Gáborík rank in voting for the Calder Memorial Trophy in 2000-01?

    a. 5th

    b. 4th

    c. 7th

    d. 3rd

16. Who won the Lester Patrick Award in 2008?

    a. Tod Leiweke

    b. Jacques Lemaire

    c. Doug Risebrough

    d. Bob Naegele Jr.

17. Who was named to the NHL's First All-Star Team in 2012-13?

    a. Ryan Suter

    b. Devin Setoguchi

    c. Zach Parise

    d. Dany Heatley

18. Which player finished 5th in voting for the Lady Byng Memorial Trophy in 2017-18?

    a. Matt Dumba
    b. Daniel Winnik
    c. Jared Spurgeon
    d. Nino Niederreiter

19. As of 2019, how many Hart Trophies have been won by Wild players?

    a. 2
    b. 1
    c. 0
    d. 3

20. Mikko Koivu has played in three All-Star Games as of 2020.

    a. True
    b. False

QUIZ ANSWERS

1. C – Marián Gáborík

2. D – Jack Adams

3. B – False

4. C – Jonas Brodin

5. A – Nicklas Bäckström

6. B – Jacques Lemaire

7. D – Jason Zucker

8. B – False

9. C – Dwayne Roloson

10. C – Mikko Koivu

11. A – True

12. D – Bill Masterton Memorial Trophy

13. B – 176

14. A – True

15. C – 7th

16. D – Bob Naegele Jr.

17. A – Ryan Suter

18. C – Jared Spurgeon

19. C – 0

20. B – False

DID YOU KNOW?

1. As a franchise, the Wild has yet to win a Presidents' Trophy, Conference Championship, or Stanley Cup. However, the club did win a division title in 2007-08. The Wild had a record of 44-38-10 with 223 goals for and 218 against for 95 points to top the Northwest Division. They were then beaten by Colorado in six games in the first round of the playoffs.

2. The only former member of the Wild to be inducted into the Hockey Hall of Fame so far is Jacques Lemaire. The former head coach was inducted as a player in 1984. Lemaire played his entire twelve-year NHL career with the Montreal Canadiens and helped the team win eight Stanley Cups. He tallied 366 goals and 835 points in 853 games, with 61 goals and 139 points in 145 playoff outings.

3. As it turned out, Jacques Lemaire was just as good at coaching as he was at playing. Lemaire has been the only Wild head coach to win the Jack Adams Award as the NHL Coach of the Year. He won it for the 2002-03 season, when Minnesota went 42-29-10-1 for 95 points. They finished third in the Northwest Division, then beat Colorado and Vancouver in the playoffs before falling to Anaheim.

4. As of 2019, the Wild has managed to win several individual major NHL trophies since its inception. These are the Bill Masterton Memorial Trophy, the Jack Adams

Award, The King Clancy Memorial Trophy, and the William M. Jennings Trophy.

5. Since 1982, the team allowing the fewest regular-season goals has been rewarded with the William M. Jennings Award. This silverware was shared by Manny Fernandez and Nicklas Bäckström for their work in 2007-08, when the Wild allowed a league-low 191 goals against. They finished second place in their division with a 48-26-8 record for 104 points.

6. The Bill Masterton Trophy is awarded annually to the player who exemplifies perseverance, sportsmanship, and dedication to hockey. Goaltender Josh Harding took the trophy home for the 2012-13 season, while fellow netminder Devan Dubnyk followed suit in 2014-15.

7. Forward Jason Zucker was honored with the King Clancy Memorial Trophy for the 2018-19 campaign. This award goes to the NHL player who best exemplifies leadership qualities on and off the ice and one who has made a significant humanitarian contribution to their local community.

8. When it comes to the end-of-season All-Star Teams, defenseman Ryan Suter was named to the First Team in 2012-13 and goaltender Devan Dubnyk made the Second Team in 2014-15. In addition, blue-liner Jonas Brodin was named to the All-Rookie Team in 2012-13.

9. Between the 1999-2000 and the 2006-07 seasons, the NHL handed out the Roger Crozier Saving Grace Award. This was received by the netminder with the best save

percentage in the league while playing a minimum of 25 games during the regular season. Dwayne Roloson won it with a save percentage of .933 in 2003-04 and Nicklas Bäckström was the recipient in 2006-07 with a .929 save percentage.

10. Former Wild owner Bob Naegele Jr. was honored with the Lester Patrick Trophy in 2008. This award was introduced in 1996 by the NHL and USA Hockey to reward the recipient's contribution to ice hockey in America. Naegele Jr. is the lone former Wild member to be named a winner as of 2019.

CONCLUSION

It's been just a couple of decades since the Minnesota Wild joined the NHL and the book you've just read contains the franchise's history from Day One to the end of the 2019-20 regular season. It's filled with facts and trivia to help fans relive the organization's relatively short history.

We trust that Wild fans have been entertained with each page and chapter and we hope that they may have picked up some new information along the way.

After a seven-year absence of NHL hockey starting in 1993, the Wild picked up in 2000 where the Minnesota North Stars left off. The state's newest hockey club has entertained the fans since 2000 and continues to do so today as it seeks its first Stanley Cup.

This trivia/factbook is a fun and lighthearted way for fans to learn about the franchise's ups and downs over the years. It's hopefully an ideal tool to arm yourself with knowledge about the team when preparing for friendly trivia tilts with others.

The Minnesota Wild are here to stay and with a fine mixture of youth and veteran leadership plus a new head coach, the squad should soon be able to contend for hockey's ultimate piece of silverware...the Stanley Cup!

Wild fans are certainly anxious to celebrate an NHL title and have been loyal to the team since it replaced the North Stars. Thanks for being among them and taking the time to check out the club's latest trivia/factbook.

Made in United States
North Haven, CT
21 February 2023

32946950R00085